Houghton Mifflin

Circle Time
and Practice

Student Book

- **Circle Time**
- **Practice**
- **Looking Ahead Activities**

Visit **Education Place®**
www.eduplace.com/kids

 HOUGHTON MIFFLIN   BOSTON

Printed in the U.S.A.

ISBN 10: 0-618-96111-9
ISBN 13: 978-0-618-96111-5

11 12 13 14 0982 16 15 14 13 12 11

4500328525

Hands On: Numbers and Number Parts to 10

Problem of the Day ———————————————— MG 1.1

Draw something that weighs more than a soccer ball.
Draw something that weighs less than a soccer ball.

Number Sense Review ———————————————— NS 3.0

Jim has 2 quarters and 7 pennies in his piggy bank.
Estimate how many coins Jim has in his piggy bank.

more than 10   less than 10

Calendar Activity ———————————————— KMG 1.2

Point to today's date on the calendar.
What day is it?

Numerical Fluency ———————————————— KEY NS 1.1

Count. Write how many in two ways.

in words: _____

with digits: _____

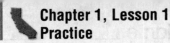
Hands On: Numbers and Number Parts to 10

CA Standards
KEY NS 1.1, MR 1.2

Count. Write the number.

1.

_____
four

2.

_____
zero

3.

_____
two

4.

_____
five

5.

_____
three

6.

_____
one

7.

_____
eight

8.

_____
six

Writing and Reasoning Jared has these
apples ⌒⌒⌒⌒⌒. He says there are **6** apples.
Is he correct? Explain why or why not.

_____

Hands On: Numbers and Number Parts to 20

Problem of the Day —————————————————————— KEY NS 1.1

Count. Write the number.

_____

_____

Geometry Review —————————————————————— MG 2.1

Circle the triangle.

Calendar Activity —————————————————————— KMG 1.2

What day of the week is it?

Numerical Fluency —————————————————————— KEY

Count. Write how many in two ways.

in words: _____

with digits: _____

Hands On: Numbers and Number Parts to 20

CA Standards
KEY NS 1.1, MR 1.2

Count. Write the number.

1.

_____ eighteen

2.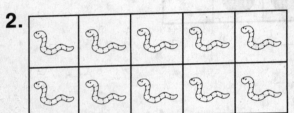

_____ sixteen

3.

_____ twenty

4.

_____ seventeen

Writing and Reasoning Kate draws the dots to the right. She says she has 14. Is she correct? Explain why or why not.

_____

_____

Before, After, Between

Problem of the Day

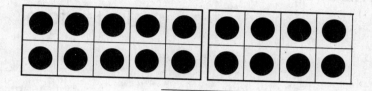 KEY **NS 1.1**

Count. Write the number.

_____

_____

Data Review

SDAP 1.1

Does this show circles sorted by size? _____

Words of the Day

SDAP 1.1

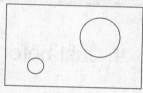 alike

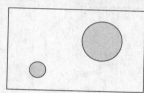 different

Turn to your neighbor. How are you *alike*?
How are you *different*?

Numerical Fluency

KEY **NS 1.1**

Count. Write how many in two ways.

in words: _____

with digits: _____

Name _____ Date _____

Before, After, Between

CA Standards
KEY NS 1.1, KEY NS 2.3

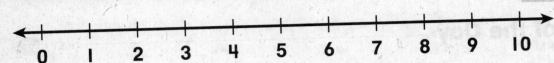

Write the numbers.

1. Just after

2, 3, _____

6, 7, _____

2. Just before

_____, 5, 6

_____, 8, 9

3. Between

5, _____, 7

0, _____, 2

4. Just before and just after

_____, 3, _____

_____, 6, _____

 Writing and Reasoning Explain how you can use the number line to find the number that comes just before 3.

_____

_____

Use with text pp. 9–10

Count Forward and Backward

Problem of the Day ——————————————— KEY NS 2.3

Write the numbers just before and just after the number 6.

___ 6 ___

Algebraic Thinking ————————————————— AF 1.2

Circle the symbol that means *plus*.

+   –   =

Counting ———————————————————— KEY NS 1.1

Count from 1 to 10.

Numerical Fluency ———————————————— KEY NS 1.1

Count. Write how many in two ways.

in words: _____

with digits: _____

Count Forward and Backward

CA Standards
KEY NS 1.1, NS 1.0

Write the numbers.

1. Write the missing numbers in order.

February

Sunday	Monday	Tuesday	Wednesday	Thursday	Friday	Saturday
			1	2	3	
		21	22	23	24	25
26	27	28				

2. Count backward. Write the numbers.

15, 14, 13, _____, _____, _____, _____, _____, 7,

_____, _____, _____, _____, _____, _____

Writing and Reasoning What number comes just after 18? How do you know?

_____

_____

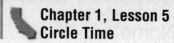
Problem Solving: Find a Pattern

Problem of the Day ———————————————— KEY NS 1.1

Count on from 7. Write the numbers.

_____   _____   _____

- - - - - - - - - - - -   - - - - - - - - - - - -   - - - - - - - - - - - -

_____   _____   _____

Number Sense Review ———————————————— KEY NS 1.1

What is the number that means 10 and 1 more?

Counting ———————————————————————— KEY NS 1.1

Count back from 10 to 1. Write the numbers.

Numerical Fluency ———————————————— KEY NS 1.1

Count. Write how many in two ways.

in words: _____

with digits: _____

Name _____ Date _____

Problem Solving: Find a Pattern

CA Standards
KEY NS 1.1, **KEY** SDAP 2.

Circle the picture that is likely to come next in the pattern.

1.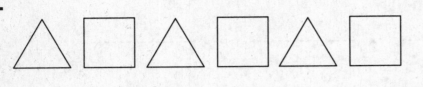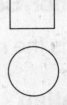

2.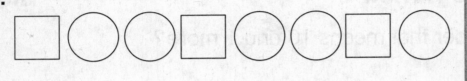

3.

4.

Writing and Reasoning Keshon made a pattern. ⬡△⬡△⬡ He says a square comes next in his pattern. Is he correct? Explain why or why not.

_____

_____

Hands On: Numbers 11 - 19

Problem of the Day —————————————— KEY SDAP 2.1

Look at the pattern. Write what comes next.

3, 5, 5, 3, 5, 5, 3, 5, 5, 3, _____

What is the part that repeats? _____

Number Sense Review ————————————— NS 3.0

Sally put 7 roses and 8 lilies in a vase.
About how many flowers are in the vase?

more than 10   less than 10

Calendar Activity ——————————————— MG 1.2

Yesterday was _____.

Numerical Fluency ——————————————— KEY NS 1.1

Write how many in two ways.

in words: _____

with digits: _____

Hands On: Numbers 11–19

CA Standards
KEY NS 1.1, NS 1.4

Use Workmat 5 and [⊙] **.**

Show.	Make 1 ten. Write the tens and the ones.	Write the number.
1. 19 ones	_____ ten _____ ones	_____
2. 11 ones	_____ ten _____ one	_____
3. 17 ones	_____ ten _____ ones	_____
4. 12 ones	_____ ten _____ ones	_____
5. 16 ones	_____ ten _____ ones	_____
6. 18 ones	_____ ten _____ ones	_____
7. 15 ones	_____ ten _____ ones	_____
8. 13 ones	_____ ten _____ ones	_____

Writing and Reasoning Raul has 13 ones. Tell about how he can group them in a different way.

_____

_____

_____

_____

Read and Write Numbers to 50

Problem of the Day ————————————————— NS 1.4

Use cubes. Show 17 ones. Regroup. Write the tens and the ones.

_____   _____   _____

- - - - - - - -   - - - - - - - -   - - - - - - - -

_____   _____   _____

tens   ones   Write the
                            number.

Geometry Review ———————————————————— MG 2.1

Circle the rectangle.

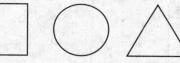

Number of the Day ————————————————— KEY NS 1.1

Show five with your fingers.

Numerical Fluency ———————————————— KEY NS 1.1

Write how many in two ways.

in words: _____

with digits: _____

Name _____ Date _____

Read and Write Numbers to 50

CA Standards
KEY NS 1.1, NS 1.4

Use charts, ▭▭▭▭, and ▢.
Show the number. Write the number.

1.

Tens	Ones

_____ tens _____ ones

_____ twenty-seven

2.

Tens	Ones

_____ tens _____ ones

_____ thirty-five

3.

Tens	Ones

_____ tens _____ ones

_____ forty-nine

4.

Tens	Ones

_____ tens _____ one

_____ forty-one

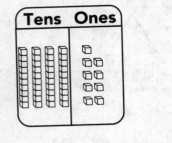 **Writing and Reasoning** Josh has 21 toy cars and 12 toy trucks. He says that he has the same number of cars and trucks. Is he correct? Explain why or why not.

_____

_____

Use with text pp. 25–27

Name _____   Date _____

One More, One Less

Problem of the Day ——————————————— NS 1.4

Write the number.

_____ tens   _____ ones   _____ forty-seven

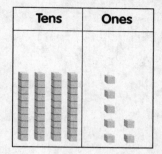

Tens	Ones

Patterns Review ——————————————— KEY SDAP 2.1

What part of the pattern repeats?
What is likely to come next in the pattern?

Words of the Day ——————————————— MG 2.4

right	left

Wave your left hand.
Put your right hand on your desk.

Numerical Fluency ——————————————— KEY NS 1.1

Count. Write how many in two ways.

in words: _____

with digits: _____

One More, One Less

CA Standards
KEY NS 2.3, KEY NS 1.1

Write the number that is I more.

1. 12	_____
2. 25	_____
3. 18	_____
4. 33	_____
5. 42	_____
6. 29	_____

Write the number that is I less.

7. _____	17
8. _____	23
9. _____	47
10. _____	32
11. _____	40
12. _____	12

Writing and Reasoning Jeb has 14 _____.

He says if he gets I more he will have 13 _____.

Is he correct? Explain why or why not.

_____

_____

Ten More, Ten Less

Problem of the Day ——————————————————— KEY NS 2.3

Write the number that is 1 more.

| 29 | |

Write the number that is 1 less.

| | 29 |

Algebraic Thinking ——————————————————— AF 1.1

Which number sentence shows that 5 apples plus
6 oranges make 11 fruits?

Counting ——————————————————— KEY NS 1.1

Count from 11 to 20.

Numerical Fluency ——————————————————— KEY NS 1.1

Write how many in two ways.

in words: _____

with digits: _____

Ten More, Ten Less

Write the number that is 10 more.

1. 23	_____
2. 15	_____
3. 36	_____
4. 31	_____
5. 20	_____
6. 29	_____

Write the number that is 10 less.

7. _____	23
8. _____	37
9. _____	56
10. _____	51
11. _____	49
12. _____	32

Writing and Reasoning Kayla has 42 stickers. Sara has 10 less stickers than Kayla. How many stickers does Sara have? Explain how you know.

_____

_____

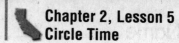
Problem Solving: Create and Solve

Problem of the Day — KEY NS 2.3

Write the number that is 10 more.

29	

Write the number that is 10 less.

	29

Number Sense Review ———— KEY NS 1.1

Write the number thirteen.

Words of the Day ———— MG 1.0

| cold | warm |

Is it cold outside today?
Is it warm inside?

Numerical Fluency ———— KEY NS 1.1

Write how many in two ways.

in words: _____

with digits: _____

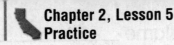
Problem Solving: Create and Solve

CA Standards
KEY NS 1.1, KEY NS 2.3

Count the stars in the picture.

Write the number. _____

Write the number word. _____

Draw the picture with one more star. How many are there now?

Write the number. _____

Write the number word. _____

Count the stars in the picture again. Write the number. _____
Draw the picture with one less star.

Write the number. _____

Write the number word. _____

Writing and Reasoning Terri draws 18 stars. She says if she draws 10 more she will have 28 stars. Is she correct? Explain why or why not.

Hands On: Break a Number into Parts

Problem of the Day ——————————————— KEY NS 1.1

Count the dots.

Draw one more dot.

How many dots are there now? _____

Number Sense Review ——————————————— KEY NS 1.2

There are 37 bicycles in the school parking lot.
Is that more or less than 50 bicycles?

more   less

Words of the Day ——————————————— KEY NS 1.2

| more | fewer |

What do you have more of, fingers or ears?
What do you have fewer of, ears or noses?

Numerical Fluency ——————————————— KEY NS 1.1

Write how many in two ways.

in words: _____

with digits: _____

Hands On:
Break a Number into Parts

Use .

Show ways to make **8**.

Write the number sentence.

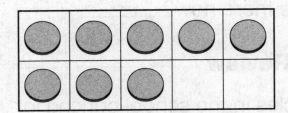

1. _____ + _____   2. _____ + _____

3. _____ + _____   4. _____ + _____

5. _____ + _____   6. _____ + _____

Writing and Reasoning Hailey used

counters to make 4. She uses   .

Is she correct? Explain why or why not.

_____

Hands On: Model Addition

Problem of the Day ———————————————— NS 1.3

Use counters if you wish. Write four ways to make 10.

_____ + _____ = 10

_____ + _____ = 10

_____ + _____ = 10

_____ + _____ = 10

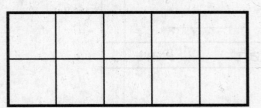

Geometry Review ———————————————— MG 2.1

Circle the square.

Calendar Activity ———————————————— MG 1.2

If today is Tuesday, tomorrow will be _____.

Numerical Fluency ———————————————— KEY NS 1.1

Write how many in two ways.

in words: _____

with digits: _____

Hands On: Model Addition

CA Standard
NS 1.3

Write the number for the total in the box
labeled Whole. Use counters to help.

1.

Whole
_____

Part	Part
1	1

2.

Whole
_____

Part	Part
3	2

3.

Whole
_____

Part	Part
3	1

4.

Whole
_____

Part	Part
4	2

Writing and Reasoning Explain how you
used the counters to add.

_____

_____

Draw to Add

Problem of the Day ———————————————————— NS 1.3

Use Workmat 4 and counters if you wish.
Show the parts. Find the whole.

Whole	
Part	Part
7	2

Data Review ——————————————————————— SDAP 1.1

Does this show squares sorted by size?

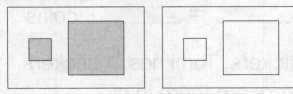

Word of the Day ————————————————————— KEY NS 1.1

how many

Count. How many people are in our class?

Numerical Fluency ————————————————————— KEY NS 1.1

Write how many in two ways.

in words: _____

with digits: _____

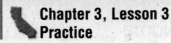
Draw to Add

Read the story. Draw a picture to solve.
Write the addition fact.

1. Marisa has 9 marbles. Jean has 1 marble.
   How many marbles are there in all?

   _____ + _____ = _____ marbles

2. Ellen has 7 pennies and 3 dimes.
   How many coins does Ellen have in all?

   _____ + _____ = _____ coins

3. Marco has 3 stickers. Tami has 5 stickers.
   How many stickers are there in all?

   _____ + _____ = _____ stickers

4. Geno has 3 trading cards. Pablo has 6 trading cards.
   How many cards are there in all?

   _____ + _____ = _____ trading cards

Writing and Reasoning Sami draws this
picture: 🍌🍌🍌🍎🍎🍎🍎🍎.
She says she has 7 pieces of fruit. Is she correct?
Explain why or why not.

_____

_____

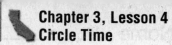
Write Addition Number Sentences

Problem of the Day ———————————————————— NS 1.3

Read the story.

Draw a picture to solve.

Write the addition fact.

Lee has 3 apples.

Sarah has 4 apples.

How many apples are there in all? _____

Algebraic Thinking ———————————————————— AF 1.2

Circle the symbol that means *equal*.

+   −   =

Counting ——————————————————————————— KEY **NS 1.1**

Count back from 10.

Numerical Fluency ———————————————————— KEY **NS 1.1**

Write how many in two ways.

in words: _____

with digits: _____

Name _____ Date _____

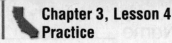

Write Addition Number Sentences

Write an addition sentence to solve.

1.

   _____ + _____ = _____

   There are **4** rabbits eating. Then **2** more rabbits come.
   How many rabbits are there in all? _____ rabbits

2.

   _____ + _____ = _____

   There are **3** butterflies. Then **4** butterflies join them. How
   many butterflies are there in all? _____ butterflies

3.

   _____ + _____ = _____

   There are **4** bugs on a leaf. Then **4** bugs join them.
   How many bugs are there in all? _____ bugs

 Writing and Reasoning Explain how you
knew the answer for Exercise 3.

_____

_____

Problem Solving: Act It Out

Problem of the Day ———————————————————— AF 1.1, AF 1.2

Write an addition sentence to solve.

There are 4 tall trees.

There are 5 short trees.

How many trees are there in all?

_____ + _____ = _____

Number Sense Review ———————————————— KEY NS 1.1

Write the number forty-nine.

Counting ———————————————————————— KEY NS 1.1

Count how many crayons you have.

Numerical Fluency ———————————————————— KEY NS 1.1

Write how many in two ways.

in words: _____

with digits: _____

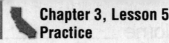
Problem Solving: Act It Out

CA Standards
KEY NS 2.5, AF 1.1

Act out the problem with counters.
Write the answer.
Write the addition sentence.

1. There are 5 apples in the tree.
   There are 2 more apples on the ground.   _____ apples
   How many apples are there in all? _____ + _____ = _____

2. There are 6 ducks in the pond. Then
   4 more ducks swim to them. How many   _____ ducks
   ducks are in the pond now?   _____ + _____ = _____

3. Hunter has 5 stickers. He gets
   3 more from a friend. How many   _____ stickers
   stickers does Hunter have now? _____ + _____ = _____

4. Olivia has 2 balloons. Faith has
   4 balloons. How many balloons do   _____ balloons
   they have in all?   _____ + _____ = _____

Writing and Reasoning Look at Exercise 1.
How did you model the problem with counters? How
did it help you find your answer?

_____

_____

Hands On: Ways to Make 7 and 8

Problem of the Day ————————————————— KEY NS 2.5

Solve. Use counters to check.

    3 rabbits are in the carrot patch.

    2 more rabbits join them.

    How many rabbits are in the carrot patch? _____

Number Sense Review ————————————————— NS 3.0

There are 23 students in Ms. Lee's class and 22 in
Mr. Jones's class.

All together, is that more or less than 50 students? Estimate.

more than 50   less than 50

Words of the Day ————————————————— KEY NS 1.1

before	after

What number comes after 15?

What number comes before 15?

Numerical Fluency ————————————————— KEY NS 1.2

Compare the numbers. Circle the correct words.

    is more than
          is equal to
          is less than

Name _____ Date _____

Hands On: Ways to Make 7 and 8

Use ▢ and ▨. Color the blocks to show 7.
Complete the addition sentence
to fit your coloring.

1. 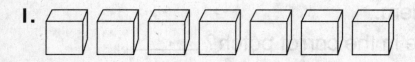 ____ + ____ = ____

2. ____ + ____ = ____

Use ▢ and ▨. Color the blocks to show 8.
Complete the addition sentence to fit your
coloring.

3. 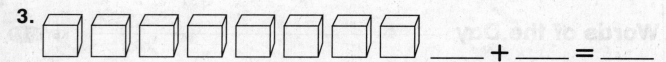 ____ + ____ = ____

4.  ____ + ____ = ____

Writing and Reasoning Jess says that
1 + 6 is the same as 6 + 1. Is she correct? Explain
why or why not.

_____

_____

Name _____ Date _____

Ways to Make 9 and 10

Problem of the Day ———————————————— NS 1.3

Use cubes if you want. Color the cubes below to
show one way to make 8.

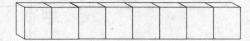   _____ + _____

Color the cubes below to show another way to
make 8.

   _____ + _____

Geometry Review ———————————————— MG 2.1

Draw a line under the circle.

Number of the Day ———————————————— KEY NS 1.1

2

Clap 2 times. Raise 2 arms. Show 2 fingers.

Numerical Fluency ———————————————— KEY NS 1.2

Compare. Circle the correct words.

   is greater than
is equal to
is less than

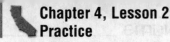
Ways to Make 9 and 10

CA Standard
NS 1.3

Use 2 colors to show a way to make 9.
Complete the addition sentence.

1. ☐☐☐☐☐☐☐☐☐   ____ + ____ = ____

2. ☐☐☐☐☐☐☐☐☐   ____ + ____ = ____

Use 2 colors to show a way to make 10.
Complete the addition sentence.

3. 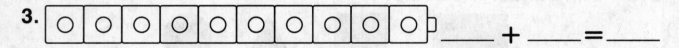   ____ + ____ = ____

4. 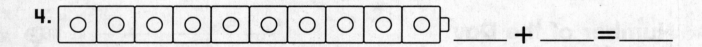   ____ + ____ = ____

Writing and Reasoning Luis says that

$7 + 2$ is the same as $2 + 7$. Is he correct?

Explain why or why not.

_____

_____

Add in Vertical Form

Problem of the Day ——————————————— NS 1.3

Color the cubes below to show one way to make 8.

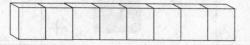 _____ + _____

Color the cubes below to show another way to make 8.

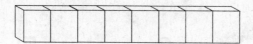 _____ + _____

Patterns Review ——————————————— KEY SDAP 2.1

What part of the pattern repeats? _____
What is likely to come next in the pattern?

      _____

Calendar Activity ——————————————— KEY NS 1.1

Use the calendar. Count how many days are left
until the end of the month.

Numerical Fluency ——————————————— KEY NS 1.2

Compare. Circle the correct words.

is more than
is equal to
is less than

Add in Vertical Form

CA Standard
KEY NS 2.1, AF 1.1

Write the addition fact.

1.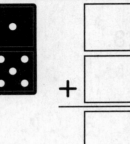

2.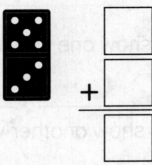

3.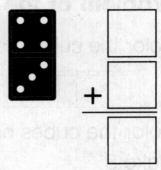

Write the sum.

4. $\begin{array}{r} 3 \\ +2 \\ \hline \end{array}$

5. $\begin{array}{r} 2 \\ +4 \\ \hline \end{array}$

6. $\begin{array}{r} 4 \\ +3 \\ \hline \end{array}$

7. $\begin{array}{r} 3 \\ +5 \\ \hline \end{array}$

8. $\begin{array}{r} 5 \\ +0 \\ \hline \end{array}$

9. $\begin{array}{r} 1 \\ +7 \\ \hline \end{array}$

10. $\begin{array}{r} 5 \\ +1 \\ \hline \end{array}$

11. $\begin{array}{r} 2 \\ +5 \\ \hline \end{array}$

12. $\begin{array}{r} 4 \\ +1 \\ \hline \end{array}$

13. $\begin{array}{r} 6 \\ +2 \\ \hline \end{array}$

 Writing and Reasoning Explain how adding across and adding down are the same.

_____

_____

_____

Add with Zero

Problem of the Day ——————————————— KEY

Write the addition fact.

  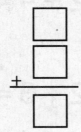

_____ + _____ = _____

Algebraic Thinking ——————————————— AF 1.2

Circle the symbol that means *minus*.

+   −   =

Calendar Activity ——————————————— MG 1.2

Point to the month on the calendar.

This month is _____.

Numerical Fluency ——————————————— KEY

Compare. Circle the correct words.

is more than
is equal to
is less than

Circle Time/Practice

37

Use with Chapter 4, Lesson 4

Add With Zero

CA Standard
KEY NS 2.1

Write the sum.

1. $2 + 0 =$ _____

2. $2 + 4 =$ _____

3. $1 + 5 =$ _____

4. $2 + 3 =$ _____

5. $0 + 1 =$ _____

6. $5 + 0 =$ _____

7. $0 + 3 =$ _____

8. $4 + 0 =$ _____

9. $1 + 4 =$ _____

10. $3 + 3 =$ _____

11. $4 + 2 =$ _____

12. $6 + 0 =$ _____

 Writing and Reasoning What happens when you add 0 and 5?

_____

_____

Problem Solving: Draw a Picture

Problem of the Day ——————————————— KEY NS 2.1

Solve.

$0 + 7 =$ _____

$7 + 0 =$ _____

Number Sense Review ——————————————— KEY NS 1.1

Write the number nineteen.

Words of the Day ——————————————— KEY NS 2.3

| I more | I less |

How many fingers do you have?

What number is one more?

What number is one less than the number

of your fingers?

Numerical Fluency ——————————————— KEY NS 1.2

Compare. Circle the correct words.

is more than

is equal to

is less than

Problem Solving: Draw a Picture

CA Standard
KEY NS 2.5, MR 2.0

Draw a picture.

Write a number sentence to solve.

Write the answer.

1. Jan sees 5 birds.
   Mac sees 3 birds.
   How many birds do they see in all?

   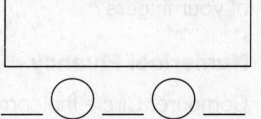

   ___ ◯ ___ ◯ ___

   _____ birds

2. There are 7 bees in the hive.
   2 more bees join them.
   How many bees are in the hive now?

   ___ ◯ ___ ◯ ___

   _____ bees

3. Pedro counts 4 ants on the hill.
   Matt counts 3 more ants.
   How many ants do they count in all?

   ___ ◯ ___ ◯ ___

   _____ ants

 Writing and Reasoning How can drawing a picture help you to solve a problem?

_____

_____

Hands On: Add in Any Order

Problem of the Day ——————————————— KEY **NS 2.5**

Read the story. Solve. Write the number sentence.

    John has 3 white cats.

    John also has an orange cat.

How many cats does John have?

Number Sense Review ——————————————— NS 3.1

There are 10 children and 25 adults at the school
picnic. All together, are there more or fewer than
50 people at the picnic?

more than 50   fewer than 50

Calendar Activity ——————————————— MG 1.2

> today's date

Use the calendar. Point to today's date.
What is today's date?

Numerical Fluency ——————————————— KEY **NS 1.2**

Compare. Circle the correct words.

      is more than

      is equal to

      is less than

Hands On: Add in Any Order

Use cubes. Make the train.
Color and write to show your answers.

1. Make a 5 train.

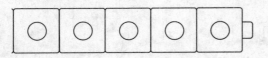

____ + ____ = ____

____ + ____ = ____

2. Make a 6 train.

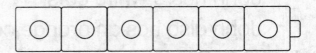

____ + ____ = ____

____ + ____ = ____

Add. Then change the order of the addends and add.

3. 5 + 1 = ____

____ + ____ = ____

4. 4 + 1 = ____

____ + ____ = ____

5. 2 + 0 = ____

____ + ____ = ____

6. 2 + 3 = ____

____ + ____ = ____

 Writing and Reasoning Why is the sum of
2 + 3 the same as 3 + 2?

_____

_____

_____

Count On to Add

Problem of the Day ———————————————— KEY NS 2.1, NS 1.3

Use cubes if you want.
Add.

$6 + 4 =$ _____

Change the order of the addends and add.

_____ + _____ = _____

Geometry Review ———————————————————— MG 2.1

What is the name of this shape?

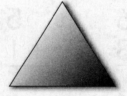

Calendar Activity ——————————————————— MG 1.2

Use the calendar.
Count. How many days are there in a week?

Numerical Fluency ——————————————————— KEY NS 1.2

Compare. Circle the correct words.

is more than
is equal to
is less than

Count On to Add

Count on to add.

1. $5 + 3 =$ ___   2. $6 + 1 =$ ___

3. $7 + 3 =$ ___   4. $5 + 2 =$ ___   5. $8 + 1 =$ ___

6. $\begin{array}{r} 7 \\ +1 \\ \hline \end{array}$ 7. $\begin{array}{r} 6 \\ +3 \\ \hline \end{array}$ 8. $\begin{array}{r} 5 \\ +1 \\ \hline \end{array}$ 9. $\begin{array}{r} 4 \\ +2 \\ \hline \end{array}$ 10. $\begin{array}{r} 8 \\ +2 \\ \hline \end{array}$ 11. $\begin{array}{r} 4 \\ +1 \\ \hline \end{array}$

12. $\begin{array}{r} 3 \\ +1 \\ \hline \end{array}$ 13. $\begin{array}{r} 2 \\ +3 \\ \hline \end{array}$ 14. $\begin{array}{r} 6 \\ +4 \\ \hline \end{array}$ 15. $\begin{array}{r} 3 \\ +2 \\ \hline \end{array}$ 16. $\begin{array}{r} 6 \\ +2 \\ \hline \end{array}$ 17. $\begin{array}{r} 7 \\ +2 \\ \hline \end{array}$

Math Journal **Writing and Reasoning** Tom counts 4 kittens in the basket. He sees 3 more jumping in to play. Explain how to count on to see how many kittens are in the basket now.

_____

_____

_____

Use a Number Line to Add

Problem of the Day ———————————————— KEY NS 2.1

Count on to add.

5 + 3 = _____

Change the order of the addends and add.

_____ + _____ = _____

Data Review ———————————————————— SDAP 1.1

What is the sorting rule?

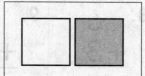

Words of the Day ——————————————————— MG 2.1

| triangle | square | circle |

Draw a triangle in the air.
Draw a square in the air.
Draw a circle in the air.

Numerical Fluency ———————————————— KEY NS 1.1

Name the number each model shows.

_____   _____

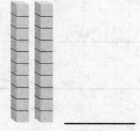
_____

Use a Number Line to Add

CA Standards
KEY NS 2.1, MR 1.2

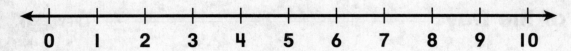

Use the number line. Find the sum.

1. $4 + 2 =$ _____   2. $6 + 1 =$ _____   3. $8 + 2 =$ _____

4. $5 + 3 =$ _____   5. $2 + 1 =$ _____   6. $7 + 2 =$ _____

7. $\begin{array}{r} 5 \\ +2 \\ \hline \end{array}$ 8. $\begin{array}{r} 6 \\ +3 \\ \hline \end{array}$ 9. $\begin{array}{r} 1 \\ +7 \\ \hline \end{array}$ 10. $\begin{array}{r} 3 \\ +5 \\ \hline \end{array}$ 11. $\begin{array}{r} 8 \\ +1 \\ \hline \end{array}$ 12. $\begin{array}{r} 7 \\ +3 \\ \hline \end{array}$

13. $\begin{array}{r} 2 \\ +7 \\ \hline \end{array}$ 14. $\begin{array}{r} 5 \\ +1 \\ \hline \end{array}$ 15. $\begin{array}{r} 3 \\ +6 \\ \hline \end{array}$ 16. $\begin{array}{r} 4 \\ +3 \\ \hline \end{array}$ 17. $\begin{array}{r} 6 \\ +2 \\ \hline \end{array}$ 18. $\begin{array}{r} 3 \\ +7 \\ \hline \end{array}$

Math Journal **Writing and Reasoning** Carrie wants to add $2 + 6$. What number should she count on from to find the sum? Explain why.

_____

_____

Use Doubles to Add

Problem of the Day ———————————————— KEY NS 2.1

Use the number line. Find the sum.

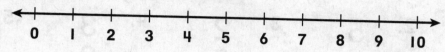

$4 + 3 =$ _____

$$\begin{array}{r} 4 \\ + 3 \\ \hline \end{array}$$

Algebraic Thinking ———————————————— AF 1.2

Which symbol do you use when you join two groups?

Number of the Day ———————————————— KEY NS 1.1

10

Name something you have 10 of.

Numerical Fluency ———————————————— KEY NS 1.2

Compare. Circle the correct words.

9   is more than
     is equal to
     is less than

Use Doubles to Add

Write the sum.

1. 4
    +4

2. 5
    +4

3. 2
    +2

4. 3
    +2

5. 3
    +4

6. 2
    +3

7. 1
    +1

8. 1
    +0

9. 2
    +1

10. 5
    +5

11. 4
    +5

12. 4
    +3

13. 3
    +3

14. 0
    +1

15. 2
    +3

 Writing and Reasoning Amber says that $5 + 5$ is a doubles fact. Is she correct? Explain why or why not.

_____

_____

48

Problem Solving: Create and Solve

Problem of the Day —————————————————

Write the sum.

$$4 \\ +4$$

$4 + 4 = $ _____

Number Sense Review ————————————————— KEY NS 1.1

Write the number 30 in words.

Calendar Activity ————————————————— MG 1.2

Use this month's calendar.
Count the days before today.

Numerical Fluency —————————————————

Write how many in two ways.

in words: _____

with digits: _____

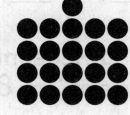

Problem Solving:
Create and Solve

1. Write a number sentence to tell how many books there are in all.

   ___ ◯ ___ ◯ ___

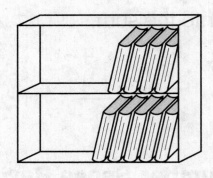

2. Switch the order of the addends. Write the new number sentence.

   ___ ◯ ___ ◯ ___

3. Write a number sentence to tell how many books there are in all.

   ___ ◯ ___ ◯ ___

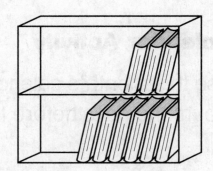

4. Switch the order of the addends. Write the new number sentence.

   ___ ◯ ___ ◯ ___

Writing and Reasoning Gina says that
$8 + 2$ is the same as $2 + 8$. Is she correct?
Explain why or why not.

_____

_____

Hands On: Model Subtraction

Problem of the Day —————————— AF 1.1 KEY NS 2.1

Write a number sentence to show how many in all.

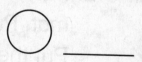 

_____ ◯ _____ ◯ _____

Number Sense Review —————————— NS 3.1

This jar has 47 buttons.
About how many buttons in all will fill the jar?

about 50   about 100   about 400

Number of the Day —————————— KEY NS 1.1

What number am I? I come before 5.
My name rhymes with door.

Numerical Fluency —————————— KEY NS 1.2

Circle the correct words.

is greater than
is equal to
is less than

Hands On: Model Subtraction

CA Standards
KEY NS 2.1, KEY NS 2.5

Use Workmat 1. Use 10 ◯.

1. Put 10 counters on the mat.
Put 4 red side up.
Put the rest yellow side up.

Write the missing numbers.
I have _____ counters.

_____ are red.

The rest are yellow.

How many are yellow?

_____

2. Put 10 counters on the
mat. Put 7 red side up.
Put the rest yellow side up.

Write the missing numbers.
I have _____ counters.

_____ are red.

The rest are yellow.

How many are yellow?

_____

Writing and Reasoning Sheri has 10 pennies. 6 pennies are heads up. She says she has 6 pennies that are tails up. Is she correct? Explain why or why not.

_____

_____

_____

Draw to Subtract

Problem of the Day ———————————————— KEY

Solve. Use counters to check your answer.

There are 8 roses. 5 are red. The others are yellow.

How many yellow roses are there? _____

Geometry Review ———————————————— MG 2.1

What is the shape of the shaded face of this cube?

Word of the Day ———————————————— KEY NS 2.5

add

Which words tell what *add* means?

take away   put together

Numerical Fluency ———————————————— KEY NS 1.2

Circle the correct words.

9   is greater than
         is equal to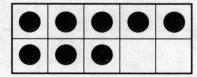
         is less than

Draw to Subtract

Draw a picture to show the story.
Solve.

1. There are **5** birds.
   3 birds fly away.

   How many birds are left?

   _____ birds

2. There are **7** ducks.
   4 ducks swim away.

   How many ducks are left?

   _____ ducks

3. There are **6** fish.
   2 fish swim away.

   How many fish are left?

   _____ fish

4. There are **9** bugs.
   5 bugs fly away.

   How many bugs are left?

   _____ bugs

 Writing and Reasoning How does
drawing a picture help you to subtract?

_____

_____

_____

Subtract to Find a Part

Problem of the Day
KEY NS 2.1

Solve. Draw a picture to check your answer.
There are 8 birds in the tree. 6 leave.

How many birds are left in the tree? _____

Patterns Review
KEY SDAP 2.1

What is the part that repeats?
What is likely to come next in the pattern?

Counting Activity
KEY NS 1.1

Start at 7. Count on 3.

Numerical Fluency
KEY NS 1.2

Compare. Circle the correct words.

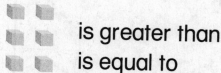   is greater than
                       is equal to
                       is less than

Name _____ Date _____

Subtract to Find a Part

CA Standards
KEY NS 2.1, NS 2.0

Use Workmat 3 and counters.

Show the whole. Move the counters to show

one part.

Find the other part.

1.

Whole	
4	
Part	Part
3	___

2.

Whole	
5	
Part	Part
1	___

3.

Whole	
3	
Part	Part
1	___

4.

Whole	
4	
Part	Part
2	___

Fill in the ○ for the correct answer.

5. There are 5 birds. Then 2 birds fly away. How many birds are left?

3   5   7   9
○   ○   ○   ○

 Writing and Reasoning If you have 5

in all and 2 are in one part, how many are in the

other part? How do you know?

_____

_____

Use with text pp. 109–110

Subtraction Number Sentences

Problem of the Day ———————————————— KEY NS 2.1

Find the missing part. Use cubes to check your answer.

Whole

Part	Part
4	

Algebraic Thinking ———————————————— AF 1.1

Write a number sentence to show how many would
be left if you had 12 apples and ate 7 of them.

Calendar Activity ———————————————— MG 1.2

Use the calendar.

Today is the _____ of the month.

Tomorrow will be the _____ of the month.

Numerical Fluency ———————————————— KEY NS 1.2

Compare. Circle the correct words.

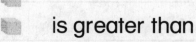

is greater than
is equal to
is less than

Subtraction Number Sentences

CA Standards
AF 1.2, KEY NS 2.1

Circle and cross out to subtract.
Write how many are left.

1. 5 − 1 = _____

2. 6 − 2 = _____

3. 4 − 3 = _____

4. 6 − 3 = _____

Fill in the ○ for the correct answer.

5. Allen has 4. He gives 2 away.
   How many does he have left?

   4   3   2   1
   ○   ○   ○   ○

 Writing and Reasoning Jill says that

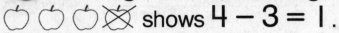 shows 4 − 3 = 1.

Is she correct? Explain why or why not.

_____

_____

Problem Solving: Subtraction Stories

Problem of the Day KEY NS 2.5

Circle and cross out to subtract.
Write how many are left.

$7 - 5 =$ _____

Number Sense Review KEY NS 1.1

Write the number 27 in words.

Words of the Day MG 1.2

first	last

What do you do first,
    put on your socks or
    put on your shoes? _____

What do you do last? _____

Numerical Fluency KEY NS 1.1

Name the number each model shows.

_____   _____   _____

Problem Solving: Subtraction Stories

CA Standards
KEY NS 2.5, KEY NS 2.1

**Find the picture that matches
the subtraction sentence.
Circle your answer.**

1. Which picture shows $7 - 2 = 5$?

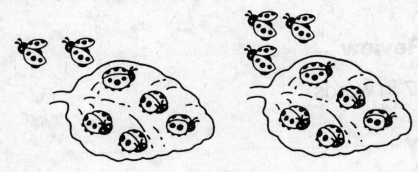

2. Which picture shows $4 - 1 = 3$?

Writing and Reasoning Explain how to
find the right picture for Exercise 2 using the words
part and *whole*.

_____

_____

Hands On: Subtract from 7 and 8

Problem of the Day

Circle the picture that shows the subtraction story.
3 − 2 = 1

Number Sense Review

NS 3.1

Kim has 15 books. Sal has 7 books. About how
many more books does Kim have than Sal?

about 10   about 20

Calendar Activity

MG 1.2

Use the calendar. Point to the year.
What year are we in?

Numerical Fluency

NS 1.0

Draw eighteen dots.

Hands On: Subtract from 7 and 8

Use 8 cubes. Circle and cross out. Write the subtraction sentence.

1.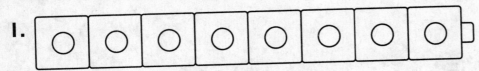

_____ – _____ = _____

2.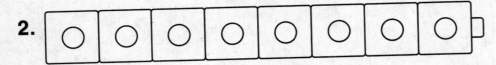

_____ – _____ = _____

3.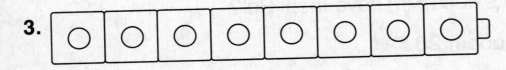

_____ – _____ = _____

Writing and Reasoning Ed makes a tower with 8 blocks. Then 3 blocks fall off. Ed says there are 4 blocks left in his tower. Is he correct? Explain why or why not.

_____

_____

Hands On: Subtract from 9 and 10

Problem of the Day ———————————————— KEY NS 2.1

Circle and cross out. Write the subtraction sentence.
Use cubes to check your answer.

Geometry Review ————————————————————— MG 2.1

What is the shape of the shaded face of this pyramid?

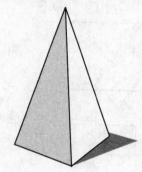

Numbers of the Day ——————————————————— NS 1.4

8 18

How is 8 like 18?
How are they different?

Numerical Fluency ————————————————————— KEY NS 2.3

What number is 10 more than 12?

Hands On: Subtract from 9 and 10

Use ten cubes. Take away some. Circle and cross out the ones you take away. Do this 3 times and write a subtraction sentence for each.

1. ⬜⬜⬜⬜⬜⬜⬜⬜⬜⬜

   _____ − _____ = _____

2. ⬜⬜⬜⬜⬜⬜⬜⬜⬜⬜

   _____ − _____ = _____

3. ⬜⬜⬜⬜⬜⬜⬜⬜⬜⬜

   _____ − _____ = _____

Writing and Reasoning Anissa has 10 apples. She gives 4 apples to Kinslee. How many apples does Anissa have left? How can you use cubes to find the answer?

_____

_____

Subtract in Vertical Form

Problem of the Day
KEY NS 2.1

Circle and cross out. Write the subtraction sentence. Use cubes to check your answer.

Data Review
SDAP 1.1

How are the circles sorted?

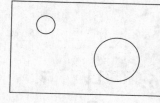 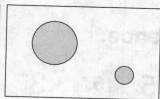

Counting Activity
KEY NS 1.1

Count on from 34 to 40.

Facts Practice
KEY NS 2.1

Add.

1. $1 + 8 =$ _____

2. $1 + 9 =$ _____

3. $4 + 4 =$ _____

4. $0 + 9 =$ _____

5. $2 + 6 =$ _____

Subtract in Vertical Form

CA Standards
KEY NS 2.1, KEY NS 2.5

Complete the subtraction fact.

1.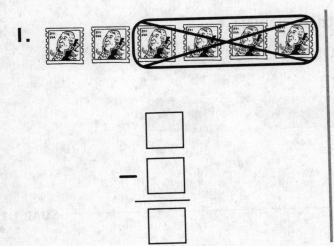

2.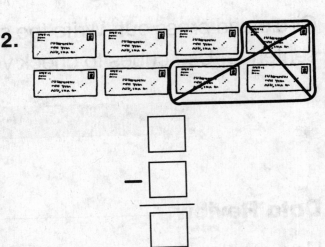

Write the difference.

3.
$$\begin{array}{r} 2 \\ -\,2 \\ \hline \end{array}$$

4.
$$\begin{array}{r} 5 \\ -\,5 \\ \hline \end{array}$$

5.
$$\begin{array}{r} 3 \\ -\,2 \\ \hline \end{array}$$

6.
$$\begin{array}{r} 4 \\ -\,2 \\ \hline \end{array}$$

7.
$$\begin{array}{r} 3 \\ -\,0 \\ \hline \end{array}$$

8.
$$\begin{array}{r} 7 \\ -\,7 \\ \hline \end{array}$$

Writing and Reasoning Is the difference the same when you subtract across or when you subtract down? Explain why or why not.

_____

_____

Subtract All or None

Problem of the Day

Complete the subtraction fact.

6 − 4 = _____

$$\begin{array}{r} 6 \\ -\ 4 \\ \hline \end{array}$$

Algebraic Thinking

Which symbol do you use to show that two
quantities have the same value?

Words of the Day

all	some	none

Are *all* children in the classroom girls?
Are *some* children in the classroom girls?
How many hippopotamuses are there in our class?

Facts Practice

Add.

1. 4 + 2 = _____ 　 2. 1 + 5 = _____ 　 3. 1 + 1 = _____

4. 2 + 4 = _____ 　 5. 0 + 9 = _____

Subtract All or None

CA Standard
KEY NS 2.1

Write the difference.

1.

$2 - 2 =$ _____

2.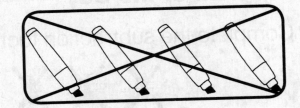

$4 - 4 =$ _____

3.

$6 - 0 =$ _____

4.

$3 - 3 =$ _____

5. $1 - 1 =$ _____   6. $3 - 0 =$ _____   7. $5 - 5 =$ _____

8. $2 - 0 =$ _____   9. $6 - 6 =$ _____   10. $1 - 0 =$ _____

11. $4 - 0 =$ _____   12. $0 - 0 =$ _____   13. $5 - 0 =$ _____

 Writing and Reasoning Explain what happens when you subtract zero from a number.

_____

_____

Use with text pp. 129–130

Problem Solving: Draw a Picture

Problem of the Day KEY NS 2.1

Write the difference.

$7 - 0 =$ _____

$$\begin{array}{r} 7 \\ -\ 0 \\ \hline \end{array}$$

Number Sense Review KEY NS 1.2

Ken ordered these numbers from least to greatest.
Which number is in the wrong place?
12, 21, 19, 27, 72, 77, 90

Calendar Activity ———————————————— MG 1.2

Do you have your birthday this month?
When is your birthday?

Numerical Fluency KEY NS 1.2

Compare. Circle the correct words.

is greater than
is equal to
is less than

Problem Solving: Draw a Picture

CA Standards
KEY NS 2.5, MR 2.2

Draw a picture to solve.
Write the answer.

1. Joanne has 7 party
balloons. Then 3 balloons
pop. How many balloons
are left?

_____ balloons

2. Beth has 8 party hats.
2 hats are blue.
How many hats are
not blue?

_____ hats

Writing and Reasoning James gets
6 presents. He opens 3 of them. He says that
he has 2 more presents left to open. Is he
correct? Explain why or why not.

_____

_____

_____

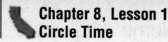
Hands On: Count Back to Subtract

Problem of the Day ———————————————— KEY NS 2.5

Solve. Draw a picture to check your answer.

Paula has 4 kittens.

1 is gray.

The others are orange.

How many kittens are orange? _____

Number Sense Review ———————————————— NS 3.1

Nick has about 100 pennies.

A toy airplane costs 49 cents.

Does Nick have enough money to buy it?

yes   no

Counting Activity ———————————————— KEY NS 1.1

Count from 22 to 30.

Numerical Fluency ———————————————— NS 1.4

Show 43 with  and .

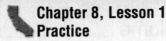
Hands On: Count Back to Subtract

CA Standards
KEY NS 2.5, KEY NS 2.1

Count back to subtract.

1.

   _____, _____, _____

   7 – 3 = _____

2.

   6 – 1 = _____

3.

   _____, _____

   8 – 2 = _____

4.

   _____, _____

   7 – 2 = _____

5.

   _____, _____, _____

   6 – 3 = _____

6.

   9 – 1 = _____

 Writing and Reasoning How do you count
back to find 8 – 3?

_____

_____

Use a Number Line to Subtract

Problem of the Day
KEY NS 2.5

Count back to subtract.
Use cubes to check your answer.

How many frogs are left in the bucket? _____

Geometry Review
MG 2.1

What is the name of the shaded face of this cylinder?

Counting Activity
KEY NS 2.4

Start at 2. Skip count by twos to 30.

Numerical Fluency
KEY NS 1.1

Write how many in two ways.

in words: _____

with digits: _____

Use a Number Line to Subtract

CA Standard
KEY NS 2.5

Write the difference.

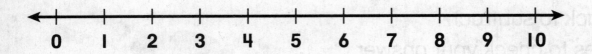

1. $7 - 2 =$ _____

2. $6 - 3 =$ _____

3. $9 - 1 =$ _____

4. $5 - 2 =$ _____

5. $4 - 1 =$ _____

6. $6 - 2 =$ _____

7.
$$\begin{array}{r} 10 \\ -\ 2 \\ \hline \end{array}$$

8.
$$\begin{array}{r} 5 \\ -\ 2 \\ \hline \end{array}$$

9.
$$\begin{array}{r} 7 \\ -\ 2 \\ \hline \end{array}$$

10.
$$\begin{array}{r} 8 \\ -\ 1 \\ \hline \end{array}$$

11.
$$\begin{array}{r} 5 \\ -\ 3 \\ \hline \end{array}$$

12.
$$\begin{array}{r} 4 \\ -\ 3 \\ \hline \end{array}$$

13.
$$\begin{array}{r} 10 \\ -\ 4 \\ \hline \end{array}$$

14.
$$\begin{array}{r} 5 \\ -\ 3 \\ \hline \end{array}$$

15.
$$\begin{array}{r} 6 \\ -\ 1 \\ \hline \end{array}$$

16.
$$\begin{array}{r} 10 \\ -\ 3 \\ \hline \end{array}$$

 Writing and Reasoning Tell how you can
use a number line to find $9 - 2$.

_____

_____

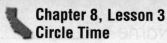
Use Addition to Subtract

Problem of the Day 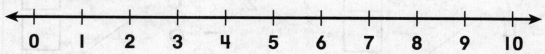 KEY NS 2.1

Use the number line.

```
←——+——+——+——+——+——+——+——+——+——+——+——→
    0   1   2   3   4   5   6   7   8   9   10
```

Write the difference.

10 – 4 = _____

```
    10
  –  4
  ____
```

Patterns Review ——————————————— KEY SDAP 2.1

What repeats in the pattern? _____

What is likely to come next in the pattern?

 _____

Calendar Activity ———————————————— MG 1.2

Look at the calendar. Name the day and the date.
Complete the sentence.

Today is _____ the _____.

Numerical Fluency ——————————————— KEY NS 2.3

What number is 10 less than 34?

Use Addition to Subtract

Subtract. Check by adding.

1.
$$\begin{array}{r} 7 \\ -\ 4 \\ \hline \square \end{array}$$

2.
$$\begin{array}{r} 8 \\ -\ 6 \\ \hline \square \end{array}$$

3.
$$\begin{array}{r} 6 \\ -\ 2 \\ \hline \square \end{array}$$

4.
$$\begin{array}{r} 9 \\ -\ 4 \\ \hline \square \end{array}$$

5.
$$\begin{array}{r} 8 \\ -\ 3 \\ \hline \square \end{array}$$

6.
$$\begin{array}{r} 7 \\ -\ 3 \\ \hline \square \end{array}$$

Writing and Reasoning Maurice completes this subtraction problem. Explain how he can use addition to check his answer.

$$\begin{array}{r} 8 \\ -\ 2 \\ \hline 6 \end{array}$$

_____

_____

_____

Subtract to Compare

Problem of the Day —————————————————— KEY NS 2.2

Subtract. Check by adding.

```
 10
− 5
____        _____ + _____ = _____
```

Algebraic Thinking ———————————————————— AF 1.1

Will walked 3 miles to the library and 2 miles home.
Write a number sentence to show how many miles
Will walked.

Counting Activity ————————————————————— KEY NS 2.4

Start at 10. Count by ten to 50.
Then count back by ten from 50 to 0.

Facts Practice ———————————————————————— KEY NS 2.1

Add.

1. 4 + 5 = _____   **2.** 1 + 9 = _____   **3.** 4 + 2 = _____

4. 7 + 4 = _____   **5.** 4 + 4 = _____

77

Subtract to Compare

Match.

Then subtract.

1. How many more  than  are there?

$7 - 5 =$ _____

2. How many fewer  than  are there?

$8 - 7 =$ _____

3. How many more  than  are there?

$8 - 6 =$ _____

Writing and Reasoning Lee has 6 🌼.
Ann has 4 🌼. Lee says he has 2 fewer 🌼 than
Ann. Is he correct? Explain why or why not.

_____

_____

Problem Solving: Write a Number Sentence

Problem of the Day _____ KEY **NS 2.5**

How many more circles than squares are there?

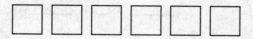

10 − 6 = _____

Number Sense Review _____ KEY **NS 1.2**

Are these numbers ordered from least to greatest? Why?
2, 9, 19, 20, 70, 72, 81, 90

Number of the Day _____ KEY **NS 1.2**

20

Are there more than 20 children in the classroom today?

Facts Practice _____ NS 3.1

Subtract.

1. 5 − 1 = _____

2. 6 − 1 = _____

3. 6 − 6 = _____

4. 9 − 6 = _____

5. 7 − 2 = _____

Name _____ Date _____

Problem Solving: Write a Number Sentence

Write a number sentence to find the difference.

1. There are **6** dogs in the yard. **3** dogs go to the doghouse. How many dogs are left in the yard?

   ___ ◯ ___ ◯ ___

   ___ dogs

2. There are **8** bees in the hive. Then **6** bees fly away. How many bees are left in the hive?

   ___ ◯ ___ ◯ ___

   ___ bees

3. There are **9** flowers in the garden. Sara picks **5** flowers. How many flowers are left in the garden?

   ___ ◯ ___ ◯ ___

   ___ flowers

 Writing and Reasoning Look at Exercise I. Explain how you knew which numbers to use for your subtraction sentence.

_____

_____

_____

80

Hands On: Relate Addition and Subtraction

Problem of the Day ——————————— AF 1.1, KEY NS 2.1

Write a number sentence to find the difference.
Kim has 4 brothers and 1 sister. How many more
brothers than sisters does Kim have?

_____ ◯ _____ ◯ _____

Number Sense Review ——————————— NS 3.1

Peggy has 50 movie star cards. She gives 12 to her
sister. About how many cards does Peggy have left?

about 30   about 40

Words of the Day ——————————— MG 1.2

Use *morning, noon, evening.*

When do you eat breakfast? _____

When do you eat lunch? _____

When do you eat dinner? _____

Numerical Fluency ——————————— KEY NS 2.3

What number is 10 less than 19?

Hands On: Relate Addition and Subtraction

CA Standards
KEY NS 2.2, **KEY** NS 2.5

Show the parts with **. Write the whole.**
Complete the related facts.

1.
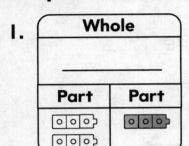

Whole
_____

Part	Part

$6 + 3 =$ _____

$9 - 3 =$ _____

2.

Whole
_____

Part	Part

$2 + 5 =$ _____

$7 - 2 =$ _____

3. 6 and 2   ___ + ___ = ___   ___ − ___ = ___

4. 5 and 3   ___ + ___ = ___   ___ − ___ = ___

5. 1 and 3   ___ + ___ = ___   ___ − ___ = ___

Writing and Reasoning Are $4 + 5 = 9$ and
$9 - 2 = 7$ related facts? Explain why or why not.

_____

_____

Hands On: Fact Families

Problem of the Day

Complete the related facts.

_____ + _____ = _____

_____ + _____ = _____

_____ − _____ = _____

_____ − _____ = _____

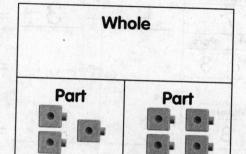

Geometry Review

Circle the shape that is curved.

Counting Activity

Count forward from 38 to 50.

Facts Practice

Subtract.

1. $10 - 6 =$ _____

2. $6 - 2 =$ _____

3. $3 - 1 =$ _____

4. $1 - 1 =$ _____

5. $9 - 0 =$ _____

Name _____ Date _____

Hands On: Fact Families

CA Standards
KEY NS 2.2, KEY NS 2.5

Complete the fact family.

1.
Whole	
7	
Part	Part
4	3

___4___ + ___3___ = ___7___ _____ − _____ = _____

_____ + _____ = _____ _____ − _____ = _____

2.
Whole	
8	
Part	Part
5	3

_____ + _____ = _____ _____ − _____ = _____

_____ + _____ = _____ _____ − _____ = _____

3.
Whole	
10	
Part	Part
6	4

_____ + _____ = _____ _____ − _____ = _____

_____ + _____ = _____ _____ − _____ = _____

4.
Whole	
6	
Part	Part
4	2

_____ + _____ = _____ _____ − _____ = _____

_____ + _____ = _____ _____ − _____ = _____

5.
Whole	
5	
Part	Part
2	3

_____ + _____ = _____ _____ − _____ = _____

_____ + _____ = _____ _____ − _____ = _____

 Writing and Reasoning How do you know when

numbers are a part of a fact family?

_____

_____

Use with text pp. 161–163

Use Addition to Help You Subtract

Problem of the Day

KEY NS 2.2

Complete the fact family.

_____ + _____ = _____

_____ − _____ = _____

Whole	
10	
Part	Part
5	5

Data Review

SDAP 1.1

What is the sorting rule?

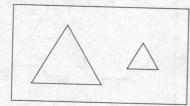   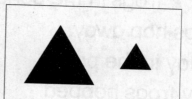

Words of the Day

MG 2.3

| right | left | between | both |

Cover your *right* eye.
Cover your *left* eye.
Cover *both* ears.
What is *between* your two ears?

Facts Practice

KEY NS 2.1

Subtract.

1. $10 - 3 =$ _____   **2.** $3 - 3 =$ _____   **3.** $5 - 3 =$ _____

4. $10 - 8 =$ _____   **5.** $8 - 0 =$ _____

Use Addition to Help You Subtract

CA Standards
KEY NS 2.2, MR 3.0

Solve. Write the number sentences.

1. Some kittens are in a basket.
4 more kittens come.
Now there are 9 kittens in
the basket. How many
kittens were in the basket
to start with?

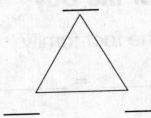

$4 + \underline{} = 9$ $9 - 4 = \underline{}$

2. There are 7 frogs in the pond.
Some frogs hop away.
4 frogs stay in the pond.
How many frogs hopped
away?

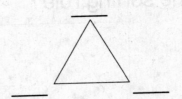

$4 + \underline{} = 7$ $7 - 4 = \underline{}$

3. Amed has 8 apples. That is
2 more apples than Katrina
has. How many apples does
Katrina have?

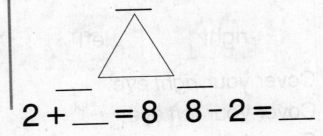

$2 + \underline{} = 8$ $8 - 2 = \underline{}$

 Writing and Reasoning Amelia has 7
balloons. She has 2 more balloons than Krystal.
How many balloons does Krystal have? Explain.

_____

_____

_____

Check Subtraction with Addition

Problem of the Day

KEY NS 2.2

Solve. Write the number sentence.

Some kittens are playing with a string.

2 more join them.

Now 5 kittens are playing.

How many kittens were playing to start with? _____

Whole 5	
Part 3	Part 2

Algebraic Thinking

AF 1.2

Circle the sentence that shows addition.

$4 + 2$ $4 - 2$ $4 = 2$

Calendar Activity

MG 1.2

Look at the calendar.

What is the name of this month?

How many days are there in this month?

Facts Practice

KEY NS 2.1

Subtract.

1. $4 - 1 =$ _____   2. $9 - 2 =$ _____   3. $6 - 6 =$ _____

4. $8 - 6 =$ _____   5. $8 - 1 =$ _____

Name _____ Date _____

Check Subtraction with Addition

CA Standards
KEY NS 2.2, KEY NS 2.1

Subtract. Check by adding.

1.   9
    −2   + ☐
         ☐
         ───
         ☐

2.   8
    −3   ☐
         + ☐
         ───
         ☐

3. 10
    −6   ☐
         + ☐
         ───
         ☐

4.   9
    −5   ☐
         + ☐
         ───
         ☐

5.   8
    −6   ☐
         + ☐
         ───
         ☐

6.   7
    −4   ☐
         + ☐
         ───
         ☐

Math Journal

Writing and Reasoning Caden completes

this subtraction problem: $\begin{array}{r} 9 \\ -3 \\ \hline 6 \end{array}$. Explain how he can

use addition to check his answer.

_____

_____

_____

Problem Solving: Choose the Operation

Problem of the Day

Subtract. Check by adding.

```
  10
-  6        +
-----      -----
```

Number Sense Review

Compare the numbers. Use >, <, or =.

81 ◯ 18

Counting Activity

Count how many girls are in the class.
Count how many boys are in the class.
How many children are in the class?

Facts Practice

Subtract.

1. $8 - 7 =$ _____   **2.** $5 - 1 =$ _____   **3.** $4 - 4 =$ _____

4. $7 - 2 =$ _____   **5.** $7 - 7 =$ _____

Name _____ Date _____

Problem Solving: Choose the Operation

Choose the operation to solve.

Draw or write to explain.

1. There are 7 puppies sleeping. 4 puppies wake up. How many puppies are still sleeping?

_____ puppies

2. 3 kittens play with a ball. 4 more come to play. How many kittens are playing now?

_____ kittens

3. There are 3 cows in the field. There are 5 cows in the barn. How many cows are there in all?

_____ cows

Writing and Reasoning Hal has 4 apples and 3 bananas. He says he can subtract to find his total number of fruit in all. Is he correct? Explain why or why not.

_____

_____

Hands On: Make a Tally Chart

Problem of the Day ——————————————————— AF 1.1

Choose the operation and solve. Complete the number sentence.

   5 sea otters are swimming underwater.

   Some come up for air. 2 otters are still underwater.

How many come up for air?

_____ ◯ _____ ◯ _____

Number Sense Review ——————————————————— NS 3.1

Carlos has 13 baseball cards. He gets 20 more from his uncle. About how many cards does Carlos have now?

about 30   about 40

Numbers of the Day ——————————————————— KEY NS 1.2

Trace 3 in the air. Trace 13 in the air.

Which number is greater? How much greater?

Facts Practice ——————————————————— KEY NS 2.1

Add.

1. $4 + 6 = $ _____   2. $8 + 0 = $ _____   3. $4 + 4 = $ _____

4. $1 + 8 = $ _____   5. $5 + 4 = $ _____

Hands On: Make a Tally Chart

CA Standards
SDAP 1.0, SDAP 1.2

1. Use the picture. Complete the tally chart. Cross out a picture and write I tally mark for each animal you cross out.

Use the tally chart to solve.

Animals	

2. How many  are there?

_____

3. How many are there?

_____

4. Which has the most? Circle.

5. Which has the fewest? Circle.

Writing and Reasoning Tami looks at the tally chart to see how many there are. She says there are I I . Is she correct? Explain why or why not.

_____

_____

Make and Read a Picture Graph

Problem of the Day ——————————————— SDAP 1.2

Complete the tally chart. Use tallies. 5 children voted for soccer. 4 prefer baseball. Only one prefers bicycling.

Preferred Sport	
Soccer	
Baseball	
Bicycling	

Geometry Review ——————————————— MG 2.1

Circle the shape that is not curved.

Words of the Day ——————————————— MG 2.3

front, back, top, bottom

Point to the *front* of your head.
Point to the *back* of your head.
Point to the *top* of your desk.
Point to the *bottom* of your desk.

Facts Practice ——————————————— KEY NS 2.1

Add.

1. $6 + 5 =$ _____   **2.** $4 + 3 =$ _____   **3.** $3 + 9 =$ _____

4. $8 + 1 =$ _____   **5.** $5 + 7 =$ _____

Make and Read a Picture Graph

Make a picture graph.

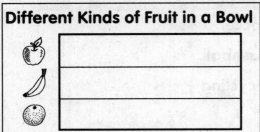

Different Kinds of Fruit in a Bowl

Use the picture graph to solve each problem.

1. How many 🍎 are in the bowl?

   _____ 🍎

2. How many 🍊 are in the bowl?

   _____ 🍊

3. Which fruits have the same number?

   _____ and _____

4. Which fruit has the most in the bowl?

   _____

📓 **Writing and Reasoning** Omar says that if 6 more 🍌 are added to the bowl, there will be more 🍌 than all other fruit together. Is he correct? Explain why or why not.

_____

_____

_____

Make a Bar Graph

Problem of the Day

SDAP 1.2

Complete the graph. Use a star for each vote.

5 children chose soccer.

4 chose baseball.

1 chose bicycling.

Preferred Sport	
Soccer	
Baseball	
Bicycling	

Key: Each ★ stands for 1 vote

Patterns Review

KEY SDAP 2.1

What repeats in the pattern?

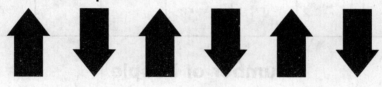

Calendar Activity

MG 1.2

How many days are left in this week?

How many days of school are left in this week?

Facts Practice

KEY NS 2.1

Add.

1. 7 + 1 = _____   **2.** 5 + 3 = _____   **3.** 6 + 0 = _____

4. 2 + 5 = _____   **5.** 4 + 4 = _____

Make a Bar Graph

1. Use the pictures. Make a bar graph.

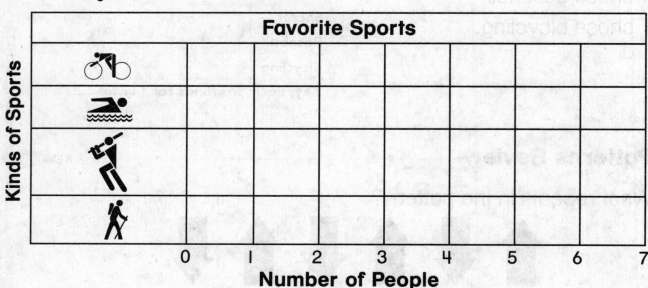

Use the bar graph to solve.

2. How many more 🏊 than 🔭 are there? _____ more

3. Circle which sport is the favorite. 🚴 🏊

4. How many 🚴 and 🚶 are there? _____ in all

Writing and Reasoning Tasha says that 🚶 is the least favorite sport. Is she correct? Explain.

_____

_____

Read a Bar Graph

Problem of the Day ——————————————— SDAP 1.2

Gina counted 5 cars, 2 bicycles, and 1 truck in the
parking lot. Complete the bar graph.

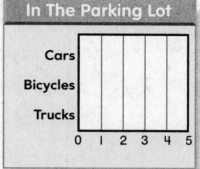

Algebraic Thinking ——————————————— AF 1.1

Write a number sentence you can use to solve this
problem. Roy used to have 10¢. He spent some of his
money. Now he has 2¢. How much did he spend?

Number of the Day ——————————————— KEY NS 1.1

Solve this riddle.
 One of my digits is 7. But I am more than 7!
 I am less than 20. What number am I?

Facts Practice ——————————————— KEY NS 2.1

Add.

1. 2 + 7 = _____   2. 7 + 0 = _____   3. 0 + 5 = _____

4. 7 + 10 = _____   5. 4 + 3 = _____

Read a Bar Graph

CA Standard
SDAP 1.2

The bar graph shows
how many children have
each kind of pet.

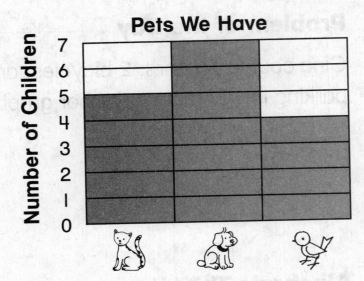

Pets We Have

Use the bar graph to solve.

1. Circle the pet **4** children
   have.

2. Do fewer children have a
   or a ?

   _____

3. How many children have
   a 🐱 or a 🐦 ?

   _____

4. How many more children
   have a 🐶 than a 🐦 ?

   _____

 Writing and Reasoning If one more
child has a cat, how many children have cats?
Explain how you know.

_____

_____

Problem Solving: Use Graphs

Problem of the Day ——————————————————— SDAP 1.2

Use the bar graph to solve.

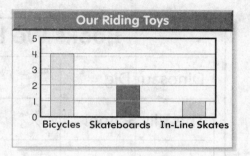

How many riding toys are there in all? _____

How many riding toys are not bicycles? _____

Number Sense Review ——————————————— KEY NS 1.2

Compare the numbers. Write >, <, or =.

19 ◯ 25

Word of the Day ——————————————————— KEY NS 2.5

Solve this riddle.

When you add, you get me. And I am the whole!
I rhyme with gum. What word am I?

Facts Practice ——————————————————— KEY NS 2.1

Subtract.

I. 2 − 1 = _____   **2.** 4 − 3 = _____   **3.** 9 − 5 = _____

4. 6 − 3 = _____   **5.** 9 − 1 = _____

Problem Solving: Use Graphs

Use the picture graph to solve.

Books We Have Read

Dinosaur Dig	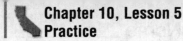
The Silly School	
My Mysteries	

1. How many more children read *Dinosaur Dig* than *The Silly School*?

   _____ more children

2. How many children in all read either *The Silly School* or *My Mysteries?*

   _____ in all

3. How many children in all read either *Dinosaur Dig* or *The Silly School?*

   _____ in all

4. How many more children read *My Mysteries* than *Dinosaur Dig?*

   _____ more child

 Writing and Reasoning Look at Exercise 2.
How did you find your answer?

_____

_____

_____

Hands On: Sort Objects

Problem of the Day ———————————————— SDAP 1.2

Use the bar graph to solve.

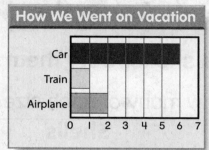

What is the way most people went on vacation? _____

How many more went by car than by either train or airplane? _____

Number Sense Review ———————————————— NS 3.0

There are 10 sharks and 20 tunas in the big tank at the aquarium. Is that more or less than 50 fish?

more than 50   fewer than 50

Counting Activity ———————————————— KEY NS 2.4

Count by tens to 60. Are there more or fewer than 60 children in the classroom?

Facts Practice ———————————————— KEY NS 2.1

Subtract.

1. $8 - 1 =$ _____
2. $6 - 5 =$ _____
3. $6 - 0 =$ _____
4. $4 - 1 =$ _____
5. $5 - 0 =$ _____

Hands On: Sort Objects

Cut out the shells. Sort them by size.

1. Show how many of each size. Color **I** box for each shell.

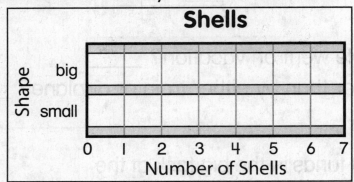

2. Use the shells you cut out. Sort them by color.

   Show how many of each color. Color **I** box for each shell.

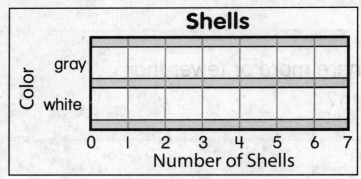

Writing and Reasoning Look at the shells
you cut out. Tell how you can sort them by shape.

_____

_____

_____

Color Patterns

Problem of the Day ———————————————— SDAP 1.1

Sort by shape. Color the squares red
and the circles blue.

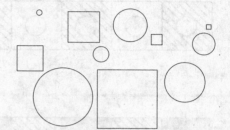

Geometry Review ———————————————— MG 2.2

Circle the shape that does not belong.

Counting Activity ———————————————— KEY NS 1.1

Count back from 37 to 28.

Numerical Fluency ———————————————— AF 1.1

Move the ✕ on top of the stars to cross them out.
Write the number sentence that shows how many stars are not
crossed out.

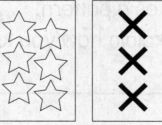

___ ◯ ___ = ___

Name _____ Date _____

Color Patterns

Circle the cube that comes next.

1.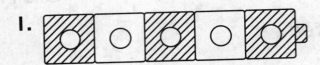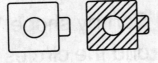

2.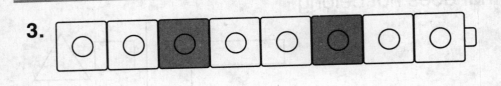

3.

4.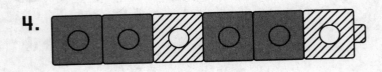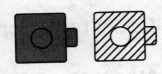

 Writing and Reasoning Tara has

○○○ and ♪♪♪. She makes a pattern: ○ ♪ ○ ♪ ○.

What fruit comes next? Explain how you know.

_____

_____

_____

Shape and Size Patterns

Problem of the Day
SDAP 2.0

Draw what comes next in the pattern.

Data Review
SDAP 1.1

What is the sorting rule?

Numbers of the Day
KEY NS 1.2

| 6 | 10 |

Show 6 fingers.
Show 10 fingers.
Which number is more?
Which number is less?

Facts Practice
KEY NS 2.1

Add.

1. $1 + 1 =$ _____
2. $2 + 7 =$ _____
3. $5 + 5 =$ _____
4. $6 + 3 =$ _____
5. $4 + 5 =$ _____

Name _____ Date _____

Shape and Size Patterns

Circle the pattern unit.
Circle what comes next.

1.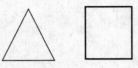

2.

3.

4.

Writing and Reasoning Ted made a
pattern ⟋▔⟍⟋△⟍⟋△⟍⟋△⟍⟋▔⟍. He says a
square comes next in his pattern. Is he correct?
Explain why or why not.

_____

_____

_____

Hands On: Motion and Rhythmic Patterns

Problem of the Day

Circle the pattern unit. Draw what comes next.

Algebraic Thinking
AF 1.2

Circle the subtraction.

4 + 4

4 – 4

4 = 4

Words of the Day
MG 1.2

| before | after |

Do you get to school *before* or *after* lunch? _____

Do you leave school *before* or *after* lunch? _____

Numerical Fluency

Compare. Circle the correct words.

9   is more than
    is equal to
    is less than

Name _____ Date _____

Hands On:
Motion and Rhythmic Patterns

Act out the pattern.
Circle what comes next.

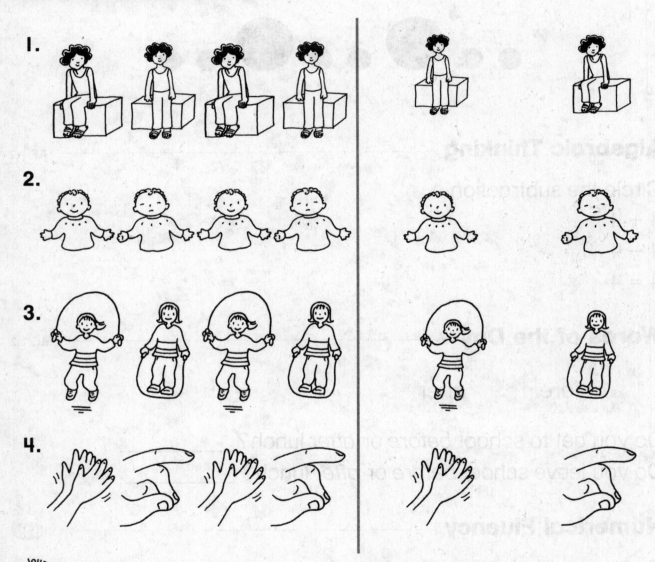

1.

2.

3.

4.

Writing and Reasoning Arianna is
dancing. She claps, then hops, then claps, then
hops. What move should she do next? Explain how
you know.

Problem Solving: Translate Patterns

Problem of the Day ———————————————— KEY SDAP 2.1

Act out the pattern.

    Raise your left hand.

    Raise your right hand.

    Drop both hands.

If this is the pattern unit, what comes next?

Number Sense Review ———————————————— KEY NS 1.2

Compare the numbers. Use >, <, or =.

50 ◯ 50

Calendar Activity ———————————————— MG 1.2

Look at the calendar.

How many Fridays are there this month?

Are there more Fridays than Mondays?

Numerical Fluency ———————————————— KEY NS 1.1

Name the number each model shows.

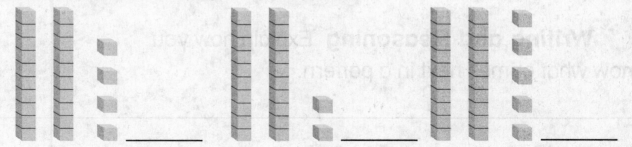

Name _____ Date _____

Problem Solving: Translate Patterns

CA Standards
KEY SDAP 2.1, MR 3.0

**Look at the pattern. Write numbers
to show it in another way.**

1.

_____

2.

_____

3.

_____

Writing and Reasoning Explain how you
know what comes next in a pattern.

_____

_____

_____

Name _____ Date _____

Hands On: Model Numbers to 100

Problem of the Day ———————————— KEY SDAP 2.1

Look at the pattern.

Draw a similar pattern with squares.

Number Sense Review ———————————— NS 3.1

There were 12 people at the afternoon show at the movie theater. There were 23 at the evening show.

Estimate. About how many more people were at the evening show?

about 5 more   about 10 more   about 30 more

Calendar Activity ———————————— KEY NS 1.1

Count from 26 to 32.

Numerical Fluency ———————————— KEY NS 2.3

What number is 10 more than 24?

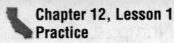
Hands On: Model Numbers to 100

Write the number of tens shown.
Write the number.

1. _____ tens

_____ forty

2. _____ tens

_____ fifty

3. _____ tens

_____ sixty

4. _____ tens

_____ seventy

Writing and Reasoning How can you show the number eighty (80) with blocks?

_____

Hands On: One More, One Less

Problem of the Day ———————————————— NS 1.4

Draw a quick picture. Write the number.

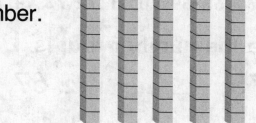

_____ tens _____

Geometry Review ———————————————— MG 2.2

Circle the figure that does not belong.

Number of the Day ———————————————— KEY NS 2.1

12

Trace 12 in the air.
What number plus 2 is 12 in all?

Facts Practice ———————————————— KEY NS 2.1

Add.

1. $1 + 10 =$ _____
2. $7 + 2 =$ _____
3. $0 + 9 =$ _____
4. $9 + 1 =$ _____
5. $4 + 4 =$ _____

113

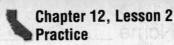
Hands On: One More, One Less

CA Standards
KEY NS 2.3, **KEY** NS 1.1

66 67 68 69 70 71 72 73 74 75 76 77 78 79 80 81 82 83 84 85

Write the number that is 1 more.

1. 75, _____   2. 67, _____   3. 70, _____

4. 69, _____   5. 73, _____   6. 82, _____

Write the number that is 1 less.

7. _____, 68   8. _____, 79   9. _____, 80

10. _____, 74   11. _____, 85   12. _____, 67

Writing and Reasoning Brody has 51 trading cards. He gives one card to his friend. Brody says that he has 52 trading cards left. Is he correct? Explain why or why not.

_____

_____

Ten More, Ten Less

Problem of the Day 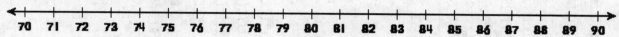 KEY NS 2.3

Use the number line.

70 71 72 73 74 75 76 77 78 79 80 81 82 83 84 85 86 87 88 89 90

Write the number that is 1 more.

79, _____

Write the number that is 1 less.

_____ , 80

Patterns Review —————————————— KEY SDAP 2.1

What repeats in the pattern?

4, 4, 2, 4, 4, 2, 4, 4, 2

Number of the Day —————————————— NS 1.0

| dozen |

How many is a dozen? What is usually sold in dozens?

Facts Practice —————————————— KEY NS 2.1

Subtract.

1. 9 − 0 = _____
2. 10 − 1 = _____
3. 9 − 5 = _____
4. 8 − 5 = _____
5. 9 − 9 = _____

115

Name _____ Date _____

Ten More, Ten Less

CA Standards
KEY NS 2.3, **KEY** NS 1.1

Write the numbers.

1.

10 less is _____.

10 more is _____.

2.

10 less is _____.

10 more is _____.

3.

10 less is _____.

10 more is _____.

4.

10 less is _____.

10 more is _____.

5.

10 less is _____.

10 more is _____.

6.

10 less is _____.

10 more is _____.

Writing and Reasoning Reba has 72 stickers. Mia has 10 less stickers than Reba. How many stickers does Mia have? Explain how you know.

_____

_____

Read and Write Numbers to 100

Problem of the Day ———————————————

Write the number.

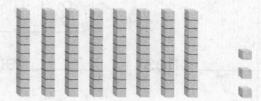

Write the number that is 10 more. _____
Write the number that is 10 less. _____

Algebraic Thinking ———————————————

Anna had 10 stickers. She used 4.
What number sentence shows how many stickers
Anna has left?

Calendar Activity ———————————————

Look at the calendar.
Which days of the week are there the *most* of?
Which days of the week are there the *least* of?

Facts Practice ———————————————

Add.
1. $8 + 2 =$ _____
2. $8 + 0 =$ _____
3. $4 + 4 =$ _____
4. $1 + 8 =$ _____
5. $5 + 4 =$ _____

Read and Write Numbers to 100

CA Standards
KEY NS 1.1, NS 1.4

Write each number.

1.

Tens	Ones
7	3

_____ tens and _____ ones

_____ + _____ = _____

2.

Tens	Ones
8	4

_____ tens and _____ ones

_____ + _____ = _____

3.

Tens	Ones
6	0

_____ tens and _____ ones

_____ + _____ = _____

4.

Tens	Ones
7	6

_____ tens and _____ ones

_____ + _____ = _____

5.

Tens	Ones
6	8

_____ tens and _____ ones

_____ + _____ = _____

6.

Tens	Ones
8	7

_____ tens and _____ ones

_____ + _____ = _____

 Writing and Reasoning In the number
72, does the **7** mean **70** or **7**? How do you know?

_____

_____

Problem Solving: Reasonable Answers

Problem of the Day ———————————————————— KEY NS 1.1

Look at the model.

Write the numbers of tens. _____
Write the number of ones. _____
Write the number sentence. _____ + _____ = _____
Write the number. _____

Number Sense Review ——————————————— KEY NS 1.2

Are these numbers ordered from greatest to least?
Explain.

1, 9, 18, 29, 70, 72, 82, 95

Counting Activity ————————————————— KEY NS 2.4

Skip count by tens to 80.
How many children all together have 80 fingers?

Numerical Fluency ————————————————————— AF 1.1

Move the **X** on top of the stars to cross them out.
Write the number sentence that shows how many stars are not
crossed out.

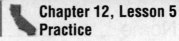

Problem Solving: Reasonable Answers

Estimate. Circle the answer that makes sense.

1. Kate goes to see a movie.
About how long is the movie?

    about 2 hours
    about 10 hours

2. First graders take a bus trip.
About how many children sit in
the bus?

    about 3 children
    about 30 children

3. Ellen babysits her younger brother.
About how old is her brother?

    about 6 years old
    about 16 years old

4. Eli reads a book before going
to bed. He starts after taking
his bath. About how many
hours does Eli read?

    about 11 hours
    about 1 hour

Writing and Reasoning Ann held some
crayons in her hand. About how many crayons
did she hold: 8 or 80? Explain how you chose
your answer.

_____

_____

_____

Hands On: Count by Twos

Problem of the Day ——————————————————— NS 3.1

There are 25 children in Ms. Kim's class and 23 in
Mr. Reginal's class.
All together, is that more or less than 100 children? _____

Number Sense Review ——————————————————— NS 1.4

How many tens and ones are in 75?

Counting Activity ——————————————————— KEY NS 2.3

Start at 34. Count on 10 more.

Numerical Fluency ——————————————————— NS 1.4

Write how many in two ways.

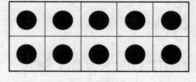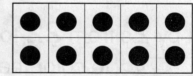
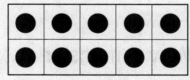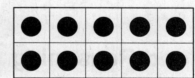
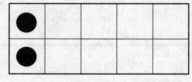

in words: _____

with digits: _____

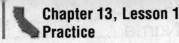
Hands On: Count by Twos

CA Standard
KEY NS 2.4, MR 1.2

**Write the missing numbers.
Skip count by 2s.**

1	2	3	4	5	6	7	8	9	10
11	12	13	14	15	16	17	18	19	20
21	22	23	24	25	26	27	28	29	30
31	32	33	34	35	36	37	38	39	40
41	42	43	44	45	46	47	48	49	50
51	52	53	54	55	56	57	58	59	60
61	62	63	64	65	66	67	68	69	70
71	72	73	74	75	76	77	78	79	80
81	82	83	84	85	86	87	88	89	90
91	92	93	94	95	96	97	98	99	100

1. 18, _____, _____, 24

2. 32, 34, _____, _____, 40

3. 64, _____, _____, 70

4. 46, 48, _____, _____

5. 54, _____, _____, 60

6. 86, _____, _____, _____, _____, _____

7. 54, _____, _____, 60, _____, _____

8. Skip count by 2s from 22 to 50.

Use ⟨▭▭▭▭▭⟩ to color the numbers you say.

 Writing and Reasoning Why is it easier
to count by 2s than by 1s?

_____

_____

Count by Fives

Problem of the Day ———————————————— KEY NS 2.4

How many hands does 1 person have? _____
How many hands do 2 people have in all? _____
How many hands do 3 people have in all? _____
How many hands do 4 people have in all? _____
How many hands do 5 people have in all? _____

Geometry Review ———————————————— MG 2.2

Circle the figure that does not belong.

Calendar Activity ———————————————— MG 1.2

Use the calendar.
What are the months of the year?

Numerical Fluency ———————————————— KEY NS 1.2

Order from least to greatest.
10, 19, 9

ordered from least to greatest

_____ , _____ , _____ .

Count by Fives

CA Standard
KEY NS 2.4

Write the missing numbers.
Skip count by 5s.

1	2	3	4	5	6	7	8	9	10
11	12	13	14	15	16	17	18	19	20
21	22	23	24	25	26	27	28	29	30
31	32	33	34	35	36	37	38	39	40
41	42	43	44	45	46	47	48	49	50
51	52	53	54	55	56	57	58	59	60
61	62	63	64	65	66	67	68	69	70
71	72	73	74	75	76	77	78	79	80
81	82	83	84	85	86	87	88	89	90
91	92	93	94	95	96	97	98	99	100

1. 25, _____, _____, _____

2. 30, 35, _____, _____, 50

3. 55, _____, _____, 70

4. 70, _____, _____, 85

5. 60, _____, _____, _____

Count back by 5s.

6. 65, 60, _____, _____, _____, 40

7. 30, _____, _____, _____, _____, _____, 0

8. Skip count by 5s from 50 to 100.
   Use ⬤▭▭▭▷ to color the numbers you say.

Writing and Reasoning Look at the numbers you colored on the chart. What pattern do you see when you count by 5s?

_____

_____

Count by Tens

Problem of the Day ———————————————— KEY NS 2.4

Find how many fingers in all. Skip count by 5s.

___ ___ ___ ___ ___

Data Review ———————————————————————— SDAP 1.1

What is the sorting rule?

Counting Activity ———————————————————— KEY NS 2.4

Count by tens to 90.

How many children have 90 fingers in all?

Numerical Fluency ———————————————————— KEY NS 1.1

Name the number each model shows.

Write the numbers from least to greatest.

_____, _____, _____

Name _____ Date _____

Count by Tens

CA Standards
KEY NS 2.4, KEY NS 2.3

Write the missing numbers.
Skip count by 10s.

1	2	3	4	5	6	7	8	9	10
11	12	13	14	15	16	17	18	19	20
21	22	23	24	25	26	27	28	29	30
31	32	33	34	35	36	37	38	39	40
41	42	43	44	45	46	47	48	49	50
51	52	53	54	55	56	57	58	59	60
61	62	63	64	65	66	67	68	69	70
71	72	73	74	75	76	77	78	79	80
81	82	83	84	85	86	87	88	89	90
91	92	93	94	95	96	97	98	99	100

1. 20, _____, _____, 50

2. 30, 40, _____, _____, 70

3. 50, _____, 70, _____, 90

4. 60, _____, _____, 90

5. 70, _____, _____, 100

Count back by 10s.

6. 80, 70, _____, _____, _____, 30

7. 60, _____, _____, _____, _____, _____, 0

8. Skip count by 10s from 10 to 100.
   Use ⬭▭▷ to color the numbers you say.

Writing and Reasoning Look at the
numbers you colored on the chart. What pattern
do you see when you count by 10s?

_____

_____

Number Patterns

Problem of the Day ———————————— KEY NS 2.4

Find how many crayons in all. Skip count by 10s.

___ ___ ___ ___ ___ ___

Algebraic Thinking ———————————— AF 1.2

Circle the sentence that shows that two things are equal.

$7 + 7$ $7 - 7$ $7 = 7$

Numbers of the Day ———————————— KEY NS 1.1

Solve this riddle.

We both have 2 digits.

We both have 1 and 2 as digits.

One of us is greater than the other.

Who are we?

Facts Practice ———————————— KEY NS 2.1

Subtract.

1. $2 - 0 =$ _____   2. $6 - 6 =$ _____

3. $10 - 10 =$ _____   4. $6 - 2 =$ _____

5. $2 - 1 =$ _____

Number Patterns

Write the number that is 1 more.

1. 39, _____ 2. 77, _____

3. 53, _____ 4. 80, _____

1	2	3	4	5	6	7	8	9	10
11	12	13	14	15	16	17	18	19	20
21	22	23	24	25	26	27	28	29	30
31	32	33	34	35	36	37	38	39	40
41	42	43	44	45	46	47	48	49	50
51	52	53	54	55	56	57	58	59	60
61	62	63	64	65	66	67	68	69	70
71	72	73	74	75	76	77	78	79	80
81	82	83	84	85	86	87	88	89	90
91	92	93	94	95	96	97	98	99	100

Write the number that is 1 less.

5. _____, 30 6. _____, 58

7. _____, 86 8. _____, 100

Write the number that is 10 more.

9. 21   10. 45   11. 57   12. 60   13. 83

_____   _____   _____   _____   _____

Write the number that is 10 less.

14. 25   15. 30   16. 53   17. 71   18. 89

_____   _____   _____   _____   _____

Writing and Reasoning How can you use *more than* and *less than* to tell about these numbers?

13   23   33

_____

_____

Problem Solving: Find a Pattern

Problem of the Day —————————————————— KEY NS 2.3

Use the chart.
Find the pattern.
Write the missing numbers.

	56	57	58
65		67	
75	76		78

Number Sense Review ————————————————— NS 1.4

What number does the model show?

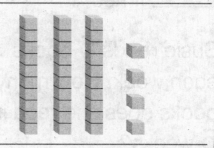

Words of the Day ——————————————————— MG 2.2

| cube | cylinder |

Can you stack cylinders?
Can you stack cones?
What is an example of a cone?
What is an example of a cylinder?

Facts Practice ——————————————————— KEY NS 2.1

Add.

1. 1 + 1 = _____   2. 2 + 5 = _____

3. 3 + 3 = _____   4. 3 + 7 = _____

5. 5 + 4 = _____

Problem Solving: Find a Pattern

CA Standards
KEY NS 2.4, MR 2.0

Find the pattern. Solve.

1. Jack walks his dog 2 times each day. How many times does he walk the dog in 5 days?

Day 1	Day 2	Day 3	Day 4	Day 5

_____ times

2. Susie reads 5 books each week. How many books does she read in 5 weeks?

Week 1	Week 2	Week 3	Week 4	Week 5

_____ books

3. Tammy reads 10 pages of her book each day. How many pages will she read in 6 days?

Draw or write to explain.

She will read _____ pages

Writing and Reasoning How did you solve the problem in Exercise 3? Explain how you found your answer.

_____

_____

_____

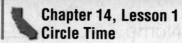
Hands On: Compare Numbers

Problem of the Day ———————————————————— SDAP 2.0

Look at the calendar.

Then fill in the table.

Sunday	Monday	Tuesday	Wednesday	Thursday	Friday	Saturday
1	2	3	4	5	6	7
8	9	10	11	12	13	14

What is the rule? _____

Sundays this Month

1st	2nd	3rd	4th	5th
1	8	___	___	___

Number Sense Review ———————————————————— NS 3.0

40 people attended the baseball game.
29 attended the swim meet. About how many more
people attended the baseball game than the swim
meet? Estimate.

about 10   about 20   about 60

Words of the Day ———————————————————— MG 2.1

Corner, side

How many corners does a square have?
How many sides does a square have?

Numerical Fluency ———————————————————— NS 1.4

Name the number each model shows.

_____   _____   _____

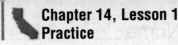

Hands On: Compare Numbers

CA Standards
KEY NS 1.2, MR 1.2

Model the numbers. Draw quick pictures.
Circle the number that is greater.

1.

27   32

2.

53   49

2.

36   30

4.

64   71

Circle the number that is less.

5.

67   80

6.

42   39

7.

58   51

8.

68   76

Writing and Reasoning Ivy has **36** stickers. Jeremy has **22** stickers. Explain how you know who has the greater number of stickers.

_____

_____

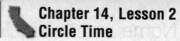
Use Symbols to Compare Numbers

Problem of the Day ———————————————————— KEY NS 1.2

Model the numbers. Draw quick pictures.
Circle the number that is greater.

75   57

Geometry Review ———————————————————————— MG 2.2

Circle the shape that does not belong.

Words of the Day ——————————————————————— MG 1.1

| long | longer | longest |

Is your arm longer or shorter than your hand?
Which is the longest, your hand, your foot, or
your arm?

Numerical Fluency ————————————————————— KEY NS 2.3

What number is 10 more than 45?

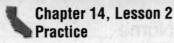
Use Symbols to Compare Numbers

CA Standards
KEY NS 1.2, **KEY** NS 1.1

Compare. Circle >, <, or = .

1.  > < =

2.  > < =

3.  > < =

4.  > < =

5.  > < =

6.  > < =

7.  > < =

8.  > < =

 Writing and Reasoning How can Sara use < to compare 21 and 12?

_____

_____

_____

Use Estimation to Compare Numbers

Problem of the Day ———————————————— KEY NS 1.2

Compare.
Use >, <, or =.

86 ◯ 90

86 ◯ 68

86 ◯ eighty-six

Patterns Review ———————————————— KEY SDAP 2.1

What part of the pattern repeats?

32, 20, 20, 32, 20, 20, 32, 20

What number is likely to come next in the pattern?

Calendar Activity ———————————————— MG 1.2

How many months are there in a year?
Say the months in order.

Numerical Fluency ———————————————— NS 1.4

What number has 3 tens and 5 ones?

Use Estimation to Compare Numbers

Circle one group of ten. Estimate about how many are in each group. Count to check.

1.

Estimate
_____
Count
_____

2.

Estimate
_____
Count
_____

3.

Estimate
_____
Count
_____

Writing and Reasoning Marcos dropped his crayons. He estimates that he dropped about **30** crayons. Is his estimate a good one?

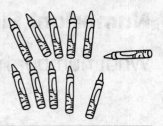

_____

_____

_____

Order Numbers

Problem of the Day ——————————————— NS 3.1

Circle a group of ten.
Estimate how many are in
 each group.
Use >, <, or = to compare.

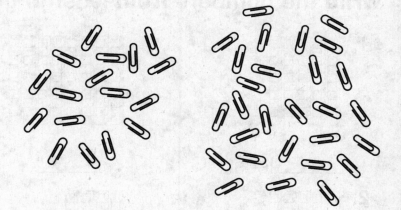

Estimate ____   **Estimate** ____

_____ ◯ _____

Algebraic Thinking ——————————————— AF 1.1

Lewis scored 23 points at the basketball game.
Then he made a 3-point shot. What number sentence
shows how many points Lewis scored in all?

Calendar Activity ——————————————— MG 1.2

| beginning | middle | end |

Look at the calendar. What is today's date?
Is today at the beginning of the month,
in the middle, or at the end?

Numerical Fluency ——————————————— NS 1.4

What number has 4 tens and 9 ones?

Order Numbers

CA Standards
KEY NS 1.2, **KEY** NS 1.1

Look at the models.
Write the numbers from least to greatest.

1.

_____ least   _____   _____ greatest

2.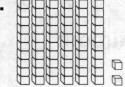

_____ least   _____   _____ greatest

3.

_____ least   _____   _____ greatest

 Writing and Reasoning Are these numbers in order from least to greatest or from greatest to least? How do you know?

68   **53**   **35**

_____

_____

Circle Time/Practice
138
Use with text pp. 269–270

Problem Solving: Create and Solve

Problem of the Day ————————————————— KEY NS 1.2

Write each number.

  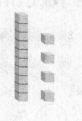

_____   _____   _____

Order these numbers from least to greatest.

_____ < _____ < _____

Number Sense Review ————————————————— NS 1.3

What is the number represented by: $2 + 2 + 2 + 2 + 2$?

Word of the Day ————————————————— AF 1.1

> number sentence

What can you write in the boxes to make this
number sentence true?

□ + □ = 8

Numerical Fluency ————————————————— NS 1.4

Write the number shown by this model.

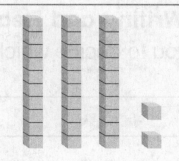

in words: _____

with digits: _____

Problem Solving: Create and Solve

CA Standards
KEY NS 1.2, NS 3.1

Compare the groups. Estimate which group has more. Count to check. Write the number sentence to compare.

1.

_____ ◯ _____

There is a greater number of 🐞 🐝 .

2.

_____ ◯ _____

There is a greater number of 🌹 🌷 .

3.

_____ ◯ _____

There is a greater number of 🍎 🍊 .

Writing and Reasoning How can estimating help you to decide which is the greater number?

_____

_____

_____

Hands On: Count On to Add

Problem of the Day ———————————————— KEY NS 1.2

Estimate which group has more.
Count to check. Use >, <. or =
to compare them.

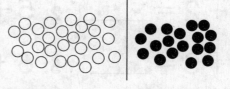

Estimate _____   Estimate _____

_____ ◯ _____

Number Sense Review ———————————————— NS 3.0

About 300 children went on the school field trip.
95 adults also came. About how many people went
on the field trip?

    about 300   about 400   about 500

Counting Activity ———————————————— KEY NS 2.4

Start at 2. Skip count by 2s to 30.
When you skip count to 30, do you say all
the numbers from 2 to 30?

Numerical Fluency ———————————————— AF 1.1

Put these two sets together.
Write the number sentence that shows how much in all.

 = _____

Hands On: Count On to Add

Write each sum.

1. $6 + 2 =$ _____

2. $5 + 3 =$ _____

3. $8 + 1 =$ _____

4. $9 + 3 =$ _____

5. $6 + 1 =$ _____

6. $4 + 3 =$ _____

7. $\begin{array}{r} 6 \\ + 3 \\ \hline \end{array}$

8. $\begin{array}{r} 7 \\ + 1 \\ \hline \end{array}$

9. $\begin{array}{r} 10 \\ + 2 \\ \hline \end{array}$

10. $\begin{array}{r} 9 \\ + 1 \\ \hline \end{array}$

11. $\begin{array}{r} 8 \\ + 3 \\ \hline \end{array}$

12. $\begin{array}{r} 7 \\ + 2 \\ \hline \end{array}$

13. $\begin{array}{r} 8 \\ + 2 \\ \hline \end{array}$

14. $\begin{array}{r} 7 \\ + 3 \\ \hline \end{array}$

15. $\begin{array}{r} 3 \\ + 4 \\ \hline \end{array}$

16. $\begin{array}{r} 9 \\ + 2 \\ \hline \end{array}$

Writing and Reasoning Brody counts 4 dogs sleeping in the doghouse. He sees 2 more going in to sleep. Explain how to use count on to see how many dogs are in the doghouse now.

_____

_____

_____

Sums to 11

Problem of the Day ——————————————— KEY NS 2.1

Write each sum. Use counters if you want.

6 + 1 = _____   6 + 2 = _____

6 + 3 = _____   6 + 4 = _____

Geometry Review ——————————————— MG 2.2

Circle the shape that has 4 corners.

Words of the Day ——————————————— MG 1.2

What are the seasons of the year?
In which season are we?

Numerical Fluency ——————————————— AF 1.1

Move the **X** on top of the stars to cross them out.
Write the number sentence that shows how many
stars are not crossed out.

 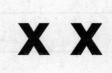

_____ ◯ _____ = _____

Name _____ Date _____

Sums to 11

CA Standards
KEY NS 2.1, MR 3.0

Write each sum.

1.
$$\begin{array}{r} 6 \\ +5 \\ \hline \end{array} \quad \begin{array}{r} 5 \\ +6 \\ \hline \end{array}$$

2.
$$\begin{array}{r} 5 \\ +4 \\ \hline \end{array} \quad \begin{array}{r} 4 \\ +5 \\ \hline \end{array}$$

3.
$$\begin{array}{r} 7 \\ +3 \\ \hline \end{array} \quad \begin{array}{r} 3 \\ +7 \\ \hline \end{array}$$

4.
$$\begin{array}{r} 7 \\ +4 \\ \hline \end{array} \quad \begin{array}{r} 4 \\ +7 \\ \hline \end{array}$$

5.
$$\begin{array}{r} 6 \\ +2 \\ \hline \end{array} \quad \begin{array}{r} 2 \\ +6 \\ \hline \end{array}$$

6.
$$\begin{array}{r} 9 \\ +2 \\ \hline \end{array} \quad \begin{array}{r} 2 \\ +9 \\ \hline \end{array}$$

7.
$$\begin{array}{r} 4 \\ +2 \\ \hline \end{array} \quad \begin{array}{r} 2 \\ +4 \\ \hline \end{array}$$

8.
$$\begin{array}{r} 11 \\ +0 \\ \hline \end{array} \quad \begin{array}{r} 0 \\ +11 \\ \hline \end{array}$$

9.
$$\begin{array}{r} 5 \\ +3 \\ \hline \end{array} \quad \begin{array}{r} 3 \\ +5 \\ \hline \end{array}$$

10. $4 + 0 = $ _____   11. $7 + 4 = $ _____   12. $8 + 1 = $ _____

Writing and Reasoning If you know that
$9 + 2 = 11$, what other addition fact do you
know? Explain.

_____

_____

Sums to 12

Problem of the Day ———————————————— KEY NS 2.1

Write each sum. Use cubes if you want.

$$\begin{array}{cc} 6 & 5 \\ +5 & +6 \\ \hline \end{array}$$

Data Review ———————————————— SDAP 1.1

Does this show shapes sorted by shape?

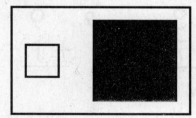 

Numbers of the Day ———————————————— KEY NS 1.1

Solve this riddle.

We both have 2 digits. We both have 2 and 4 as digits.

But one of us is less than the other. Who are we?

Facts Practice ———————————————— KEY NS 2.1

Subtract.

1. $7 - 1 =$ _____   2. $7 - 2 =$ _____

3. $3 - 2 =$ _____   4. $9 - 7 =$ _____

5. $9 - 2 =$ _____

Sums to 12

CA Standards
KEY NS 2.1, MR 3.0

Write each sum.

1. $2 \quad 10$
    $\underline{+10} \quad \underline{+2}$

2. $7 \quad 2$
    $\underline{+2} \quad \underline{+7}$

3. $6 \quad 3$
    $\underline{+3} \quad \underline{+6}$

4. $6 \quad 5$
    $\underline{+5} \quad \underline{+6}$

5. $11 \quad 1$
    $\underline{+1} \quad \underline{+11}$

6. $5 \quad 4$
    $\underline{+4} \quad \underline{+5}$

7. $7 \quad 5$
    $\underline{+5} \quad \underline{+7}$

8. $7 \quad 3$
    $\underline{+3} \quad \underline{+7}$

9. $9 \quad 1$
    $\underline{+1} \quad \underline{+9}$

10. $5 + 7 = \underline{}$
    $7 + 5 = \underline{}$

11. $3 + 9 = \underline{}$
    $9 + 3 = \underline{}$

12. $8 + 4 = \underline{}$
    $4 + 8 = \underline{}$

 Writing and Reasoning If you know that
$5 + 7 = 12$, what other addition fact do you
know? Explain.

_____

_____

_____

Add Three Numbers

Problem of the Day

Write each sum. Use cubes to check your answer.

$$\begin{array}{cc} 7 \\ +5 \end{array} \qquad \begin{array}{cc} 5 \\ +7 \end{array} \qquad \begin{array}{cc} 8 \\ +4 \end{array} \qquad \begin{array}{cc} 4 \\ +8 \end{array}$$

Algebraic Thinking

AF 1.2

Holly picked 5 daisies and 2 sunflowers.
Which symbol do you use to find how many
flowers Holly picked in all?

Counting Activity

Start at 5. Skip count by 5s to 60.
When you skip count by 5s to 60,
do you say all the numbers from 5 to 60? Why?

Numerical Fluency

NS 1.4

Which is NOT a way to make 24? Circle it.

24 ones

2 tens 4 ones

24 tens

Add Three Numbers

CA Standard
NS 2.7

Write each sum. Circle the 2 numbers you added first.

1. $\begin{array}{r} 1 \\ 3 \\ +4 \\ \hline \end{array}$

2. $\begin{array}{r} 3 \\ 5 \\ +4 \\ \hline \end{array}$

3. $\begin{array}{r} 7 \\ 0 \\ +4 \\ \hline \end{array}$

4. $\begin{array}{r} 6 \\ 1 \\ +4 \\ \hline \end{array}$

5. $\begin{array}{r} 5 \\ 2 \\ +3 \\ \hline \end{array}$

6. $\begin{array}{r} 4 \\ 1 \\ +5 \\ \hline \end{array}$

7. $\begin{array}{r} 2 \\ 4 \\ +4 \\ \hline \end{array}$

8. $\begin{array}{r} 3 \\ 5 \\ +1 \\ \hline \end{array}$

9. $\begin{array}{r} 7 \\ 1 \\ +3 \\ \hline \end{array}$

10. $\begin{array}{r} 2 \\ 9 \\ +0 \\ \hline \end{array}$

11. $\begin{array}{r} 3 \\ 3 \\ +5 \\ \hline \end{array}$

12. $\begin{array}{r} 6 \\ 2 \\ +1 \\ \hline \end{array}$

13. $7 + 2 + 2 =$ _____

14. $2 + 7 + 1 =$ _____

15. $2 + 3 + 1 =$ _____

16. $4 + 2 + 1 =$ _____

Writing and Reasoning Sami needs to add the numbers 2, 3, and 7. Which numbers should she add first? Explain.

_____

_____

_____

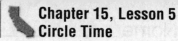
Missing Addends

Problem of the Day ————————————————— NS 2.7

Write the sum. Circle the two numbers you added first.

$$
\begin{array}{r}
4 \\
5 \\
+\ 3 \\
\hline
\end{array}
$$

Number Sense Review ———————————— KEY

Each box holds ten crayons.
How many crayons are there in all?

Words of the Day ————————————————— MG 1.2

hot	warm	cool	cold

Which word best describes the weather today?

Numerical Fluency ————————————————— KEY

Compare. Circle the correct words.

is greater than
is equal to
is less than

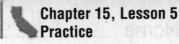
Missing Addends

Write the missing addend.

1. ☐☐☐☐☐☐☐

$\boxed{} + 4 = 7$

2. ☐☐☐☐☐☐☐☐

$\boxed{} + 6 = 8$

3. $5 + \boxed{} = 8$ 4. $2 + \boxed{} = 10$ 5. $3 + \boxed{} = 11$

6.
$$\begin{array}{r} 1 \\ + \boxed{} \\ \hline 8 \end{array}$$

7.
$$\begin{array}{r} 4 \\ + \boxed{} \\ \hline 6 \end{array}$$

8.
$$\begin{array}{r} \boxed{} \\ + 3 \\ \hline 10 \end{array}$$

9.
$$\begin{array}{r} 6 \\ + \boxed{} \\ \hline 9 \end{array}$$

10.
$$\begin{array}{r} \boxed{} \\ + 2 \\ \hline 11 \end{array}$$

11.
$$\begin{array}{r} \boxed{} \\ + 4 \\ \hline 7 \end{array}$$

12.
$$\begin{array}{r} \boxed{} \\ + 6 \\ \hline 12 \end{array}$$

13.
$$\begin{array}{r} \boxed{} \\ + 3 \\ \hline 5 \end{array}$$

14.
$$\begin{array}{r} \boxed{} \\ + 5 \\ \hline 10 \end{array}$$

15.
$$\begin{array}{r} 2 \\ + \boxed{} \\ \hline 7 \end{array}$$

Writing and Reasoning Sami needs to add a number to 4 to get a sum of 9. Which number should she add to 4? Explain.

_____

_____

_____

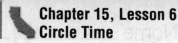
Write a Number Sentence

Problem of the Day ——————————————— AF 1.1

Find the missing number. Use cubes if you want.

5 + □ = 11

Number Sense Review ——————————————— KEY NS 2.4

There are 6 people in the room.
How many fingers are there in all?
   1 person, 2 people, 3 people,
   4 people, 5 people, 6 people

_____ , _____ , _____ , _____ , _____ , _____

Words of the Day ——————————————— MG 1.2

hotter	colder

Are winter days generally hotter or colder than
summer days? Are summer days generally hotter
or colder than spring days?

Numerical Fluency ——————————————— NS 1.4

Model 8 + 3 with ▭▭▭▭▭▭ and ▪ .

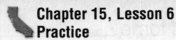
Problem Solving: Write a Number Sentence

CA Standards
AF 1.1, MR 2.2

Complete the table. Solve.

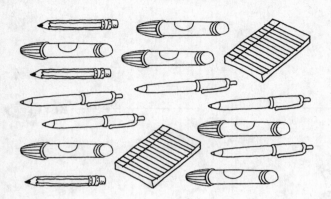

Items	Number
Pens	
Pencils	
Notebooks	
Markers	

1. How many pencils and pens are there?

_____ pencils and pens

Draw or write to explain

___○___○___

2. How many more markers than notebooks are there?

_____ markers

___○___○___

 **Writing and Reasoning** Luke adds **3** more markers to the table. Explain how to decide how many markers there are now.

_____

_____

_____

_____

Hands On: Count Back to Subtract

Problem of the Day

Write a number sentence to solve.

Henry has 5 pairs of tie shoes.

He also has 7 pairs of slip-on shoes.

How many pairs of shoes does Henry have?

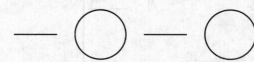

Number Sense Review

Heather borrowed 28 CDs from her friend.

She returned 9.

About how many of her friend's CDs does she still have?

about 10   about 20   about 40

Calendar Activity

Look at the calendar.

In which week is today's date?

Numerical Fluency

Use and .

Compare. Use >, <, or =.

76 ◯ 69

Hands On: Count Back to Subtract

CA Standards
KEY NS 2.5, **KEY** NS 2.1

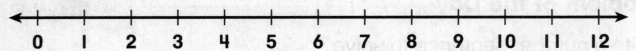

Subtract.

1. $\begin{array}{r} 9 \\ -1 \\ \hline \end{array}$

2. $\begin{array}{r} 7 \\ -2 \\ \hline \end{array}$

3. $\begin{array}{r} 10 \\ -3 \\ \hline \end{array}$

4. $\begin{array}{r} 6 \\ -2 \\ \hline \end{array}$

5. $\begin{array}{r} 11 \\ -3 \\ \hline \end{array}$

6. $\begin{array}{r} 8 \\ -1 \\ \hline \end{array}$

7. $\begin{array}{r} 5 \\ -2 \\ \hline \end{array}$

8. $\begin{array}{r} 11 \\ -2 \\ \hline \end{array}$

9. $\begin{array}{r} 9 \\ -3 \\ \hline \end{array}$

10. $\begin{array}{r} 10 \\ -2 \\ \hline \end{array}$

11. $\begin{array}{r} 9 \\ -2 \\ \hline \end{array}$

12. $\begin{array}{r} 10 \\ -1 \\ \hline \end{array}$

13. $8 - 3 =$ _____ 14. $7 - 1 =$ _____ 15. $11 - 1 =$ _____

Writing and Reasoning How do you count back to find $10 - 3$?

_____

_____

_____

Name _____ Date _____

Subtract from 11 and Less

Problem of the Day ———————————— KEY NS 2.1

Subtract. Use counters if you want.

11 − 3 = _____   11

                     − 3

Geometry Review ———————————— MG 2.2

Circle the figure that has 3 corners and 3 straight sides.

Number of the Day ———————————— KEY NS 1.2

Trace 99 in the air. Are there more than 99 children in the classroom? Are there more than 99 children in the school? How many tens are in 99?

Facts Practice ———————————— KEY NS 2.1

Add.

1. 3 + 9 = _____   2.   4 + 5 = _____
3. 6 + 1 = _____   4.   1 + 1 = _____
5. 2 + 8 = _____

Subtract from 11 and Less

Write each difference.

1. $\begin{array}{r} 11 \\ -5 \end{array}$ $\begin{array}{r} 11 \\ -6 \end{array}$ 2. $\begin{array}{r} 9 \\ -7 \end{array}$ $\begin{array}{r} 9 \\ -2 \end{array}$ 3. $\begin{array}{r} 10 \\ -3 \end{array}$ $\begin{array}{r} 10 \\ -7 \end{array}$

4. $\begin{array}{r} 11 \\ -9 \end{array}$ $\begin{array}{r} 11 \\ -2 \end{array}$ 5. $\begin{array}{r} 11 \\ -7 \end{array}$ $\begin{array}{r} 11 \\ -4 \end{array}$ 6. $\begin{array}{r} 9 \\ -3 \end{array}$ $\begin{array}{r} 9 \\ -6 \end{array}$

7. $\begin{array}{r} 10 \\ -9 \end{array}$ $\begin{array}{r} 10 \\ -1 \end{array}$ 8. $\begin{array}{r} 8 \\ -2 \end{array}$ $\begin{array}{r} 8 \\ -6 \end{array}$ 9. $\begin{array}{r} 11 \\ -8 \end{array}$ $\begin{array}{r} 11 \\ -3 \end{array}$

10. $10 - 2 = $ _____   11. $9 - 6 = $ _____

$10 - 8 = $ _____ $9 - 3 = $ _____

Writing and Reasoning How does knowing that $11 - 6 = 5$ help you find the answer to $11 - 5$?

_____

_____

_____

Subtract from 12 and Less

Problem of the Day

Subtract. Use cubes to check your answer.

$11 - 7 =$ _____

$\begin{array}{r} 11 \\ -\ 7 \\ \hline \end{array}$

Patterns Review

What part repeats to make a pattern? What is likely
to come next in the pattern?

★ ★ ● ★ ★ ● ★ ★ ● ★ _____

Words of the Day

| greatest | least |

What is the greatest,
the number of children in the classroom, the number of
children in the school, or the number of children in the town?
Which is the least?

Facts Practice

Add.

1. $4 + 1 =$ _____   2. $1 + 6 =$ _____
3. $8 + 2 =$ _____   4. $10 + 1 =$ _____
5. $2 + 9 =$ _____

Subtract from 12 and Less

CA Standards
KEY NS 2.1, MR 3.0

Write each difference.

1.
$$12 \\ -3$$ $$12 \\ -9$$

2.
$$11 \\ -2$$ $$11 \\ -9$$

3.
$$10 \\ -4$$ $$10 \\ -6$$

4.
$$11 \\ -4$$ $$11 \\ -7$$

5.
$$8 \\ -3$$ $$8 \\ -5$$

6.
$$10 \\ -8$$ $$10 \\ -2$$

7. $11 - 5 =$ _____

8. $9 - 8 =$ _____

$11 - 6 =$ _____

$9 - 1 =$ _____

Writing and Reasoning How does knowing that $12 - 5 = 7$ help you find the answer to $12 - 7$?

_____

_____

_____

Relate Addition and Subtraction

Problem of the Day ———————————— KEY NS 2.1

Subtract. Use cubes if you want.

   11 − 7 = _____   12 − 7 = _____

$$\begin{array}{r} 11 \\ -\ 7 \\ \hline \end{array} \qquad\qquad \begin{array}{r} 12 \\ -\ 7 \\ \hline \end{array}$$

Algebraic Thinking Review ———————————— AF 1.1

7 penguins are swimming at the zoo.
5 more join them. Which number sentence shows
how many penguins are swimming now?

Counting Activity ———————————— KEY NS 2.4

Start at 5. Skip count by 5s to 100. Is skip counting by
5s to 100 faster or slower than counting by tens to 100?

Facts Practice ———————————— KEY NS 2.1

Subtract.

1. 7 − 1 = _____
2. 9 − 3 = _____
3. 8 − 8 = _____
4. 7 − 5 = _____
5. 5 − 3 = _____

Relate Addition and Subtraction

Use related facts to add and subtract.

1. $\begin{array}{r} 7 \\ +4 \end{array}$ $\begin{array}{r} 11 \\ -4 \end{array}$ 2. $\begin{array}{r} 6 \\ +3 \end{array}$ $\begin{array}{r} 9 \\ -3 \end{array}$ 3. $\begin{array}{r} 9 \\ +3 \end{array}$ $\begin{array}{r} 12 \\ -3 \end{array}$

4. $\begin{array}{r} 6 \\ +6 \end{array}$ $\begin{array}{r} 12 \\ -6 \end{array}$ 5. $\begin{array}{r} 7 \\ +5 \end{array}$ $\begin{array}{r} 12 \\ -5 \end{array}$ 6. $\begin{array}{r} 6 \\ +4 \end{array}$ $\begin{array}{r} 10 \\ -4 \end{array}$

7. $\begin{array}{r} 5 \\ +4 \end{array}$ $\begin{array}{r} 9 \\ -4 \end{array}$ 8. $\begin{array}{r} 2 \\ +9 \end{array}$ $\begin{array}{r} 11 \\ -9 \end{array}$ 9. $\begin{array}{r} 7 \\ +2 \end{array}$ $\begin{array}{r} 9 \\ -2 \end{array}$

10. $\begin{array}{r} 7 \\ +3 \end{array}$ $\begin{array}{r} 10 \\ -3 \end{array}$ 11. $\begin{array}{r} 2 \\ +8 \end{array}$ $\begin{array}{r} 10 \\ -8 \end{array}$ 12. $\begin{array}{r} 8 \\ +4 \end{array}$ $\begin{array}{r} 12 \\ -4 \end{array}$

Writing and Reasoning Abigail knows that
$7 + 5 = 12$. How will knowing this help her find
$12 - 5$?

_____

_____

Problem Solving: Use a Table

Problem of the Day ———————————— KEY 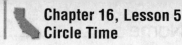 NS 2.2

Use related facts to add and subtract.

$$\begin{array}{r} 11 \\ -7 \\ \hline \end{array} \qquad \begin{array}{r} 7 \\ +4 \\ \hline \end{array}$$

$11 - 7 =$ _____ $7 + 4 =$ _____

Number Sense Review ———————————— KEY NS 2.4

Find the counting pattern. Which number is likely to come next?

25, 30, 35, 40, 45, 50, _____

Counting Activity ———————————————— MG 1.2

How many days are there from today to the end of the month? How many weeks?

Facts Practice ———————————————— KEY NS 2.1

Subtract.

1. $4 - 1 =$ _____
2. $9 - 7 =$ _____
3. $8 - 8 =$ _____
4. $7 - 4 =$ _____
5. $8 - 3 =$ _____

Problem Solving: Use a Table

CA Standards
KEY NS 2.1, MR 1.1

Mia is taking pictures for a class project.

The table shows the number of pictures Mia takes.

Day	Number
Friday	9
Saturday	
Sunday	

Solve.

Complete the table.

1. Mia took 2 more pictures on Saturday than she did on Friday. How many pictures did Mia take on Saturday?

   _____ pictures

2. Mia took 3 fewer pictures on Sunday than on Saturday. How many pictures did Mia take on Sunday?

   _____ pictures

Writing and Reasoning On Monday, Mia takes 3 more pictures than she took on Friday. How many pictures did she take on Monday? Explain your answer.

_____

_____

Hands On: Add Doubles

Problem of the Day ——————————————————— AF 1.1

Use the table.

Ski Supplies	
Pairs of skis	8
Snowboards	11

_____ ◯ _____ ◯ _____

Complete the number sentence.

How many more snowboards than pairs of skis are there?

_____ more snowboards

Number Sense Review ——————————————————— NS 3.1

John ran for 47 minutes. Amy ran for 38 minutes. About how many more minutes did John run than Amy?

Counting Activity ——————————————————— KEY NS 1.1

Count on from 27 to 32.

Facts Practice ——————————————————— KEY NS 2.1

Add.

1. 5 + 1 = _____

2. 4 + 3 = _____

3. 1 + 1 = _____

4. 0 + 4 = _____

5. 9 + 3 = _____

163

Hands On: Add Doubles

CA Standards
KEY NS 2.1

Write each sum. Circle the doubles facts.

1. $\begin{array}{r} 6 \\ +6 \\ \hline \end{array}$

2. $\begin{array}{r} 9 \\ +9 \\ \hline \end{array}$

3. $\begin{array}{r} 6 \\ +3 \\ \hline \end{array}$

4. $\begin{array}{r} 7 \\ +7 \\ \hline \end{array}$

5. $\begin{array}{r} 8 \\ +1 \\ \hline \end{array}$

6. $\begin{array}{r} 5 \\ +5 \\ \hline \end{array}$

7. $\begin{array}{r} 3 \\ +4 \\ \hline \end{array}$

8. $\begin{array}{r} 7 \\ +2 \\ \hline \end{array}$

9. $\begin{array}{r} 9 \\ +3 \\ \hline \end{array}$

10. $\begin{array}{r} 6 \\ +5 \\ \hline \end{array}$

11. $\begin{array}{r} 10 \\ +10 \\ \hline \end{array}$

12. $\begin{array}{r} 8 \\ +8 \\ \hline \end{array}$

13. $\begin{array}{r} 2 \\ +9 \\ \hline \end{array}$

14. $\begin{array}{r} 5 \\ +7 \\ \hline \end{array}$

15. $\begin{array}{r} 3 \\ +8 \\ \hline \end{array}$

16. $\begin{array}{r} 4 \\ +4 \\ \hline \end{array}$

Writing and Reasoning Hal adds these numbers, $8 + 4 = 12$. He says that this exercise is a doubles fact. Is he correct? Explain why or why not.

_____

_____

Name _____ Date _____

Doubles Plus One

Problem of the Day ———————————————————— KEY NS 2.1

Find the sum. Circle the doubles fact.

5 + 6 = _____

5 + 5 = _____

6 + 5 = _____

Geometry Review ———————————————————————— MG 2.2

Circle the figure that has no corners.

Calendar Activity ———————————————————————— MG 1.2

Look at the calendar. What is the date of the
second Sunday of this month?

Facts Practice ————————————————————————————— NS 2.7

Make a ten. Then find the sum.

1. 6 + 4 + 7 = _____

2. 2 + 9 + 8 = _____

3. 3 + 7 + 4 = _____

4. 9 + 4 + 1 = _____

5. 5 + 5 + 5 = _____

Doubles Plus One

CA Standards
KEY NS 2.1, MR 3.0

Find the sum.

1. $4 + 4 =$ _____ $4 + 5 =$ _____ $5 + 4 =$ _____

2. $6 + 6 =$ _____ $6 + 7 =$ _____ $7 + 6 =$ _____

3. $7 + 7 =$ _____ $7 + 8 =$ _____ $8 + 7 =$ _____

4. $\begin{array}{r} 3 \\ +3 \\ \hline \end{array}$
5. $\begin{array}{r} 4 \\ +3 \\ \hline \end{array}$
6. $\begin{array}{r} 5 \\ +2 \\ \hline \end{array}$
7. $\begin{array}{r} 5 \\ +5 \\ \hline \end{array}$
8. $\begin{array}{r} 6 \\ +5 \\ \hline \end{array}$

9. $\begin{array}{r} 3 \\ +4 \\ \hline \end{array}$
10. $\begin{array}{r} 7 \\ +8 \\ \hline \end{array}$
11. $\begin{array}{r} 8 \\ +8 \\ \hline \end{array}$
12. $\begin{array}{r} 9 \\ +8 \\ \hline \end{array}$
13. $\begin{array}{r} 9 \\ +9 \\ \hline \end{array}$

Writing and Reasoning Marvin is finding the sum of $6 + 7$. How can he use a doubles fact to find the sum?

_____

_____

Hands On: Add with 10

Problem of the Day —————————————————————— KEY **NS 2.1**

Find the sum.
Circle the addition that is doubles plus one.

6 + 6 = _____

6 + 5 = _____

5 + 5 = _____

Patterns Review —————————————————————— KEY **SDAP 2.1**

Tina is learning a new way to jump.

left foot, right foot, both feet, left foot, right foot,

both feet, left foot, ...

What repeats in Tina's pattern?

Calendar —————————————————————————————— NS 1.4

Find today's date. How many different ways can
you say and show the number?

Facts Practice —————————————————————— KEY **NS 2.1**

Subtract.

1. 9 − 1 = _____

2. 8 − 3 = _____

3. 4 − 0 = _____

4. 7 − 2 = _____

5. 6 − 1 = _____

Name _____ Date _____

Hands On: Add with 10

CA Standards
KEY NS 2.1, NS 1.4

Use workmat 3 and ◯. Show the numbers.
Write the number sentence.

1. Show 10. Show 2 more.

____ ◯ ____ ◯ ____

2. Show 10. Show 6 more.

____ ◯ ____ ◯ ____

3. Show 10. Show 1 more.

____ ◯ ____ ◯ ____

4. Show 10. Show 9 more.

____ ◯ ____ ◯ ____

Find the sum.

5.
$$\begin{array}{r} 10 \\ +4 \\ \hline \end{array}$$

6.
$$\begin{array}{r} 10 \\ +8 \\ \hline \end{array}$$

7.
$$\begin{array}{r} 5 \\ +10 \\ \hline \end{array}$$

8.
$$\begin{array}{r} 1 \\ +10 \\ \hline \end{array}$$

9.
$$\begin{array}{r} 4 \\ +10 \\ \hline \end{array}$$

10.
$$\begin{array}{r} 6 \\ +10 \\ \hline \end{array}$$

11.
$$\begin{array}{r} 10 \\ +3 \\ \hline \end{array}$$

12.
$$\begin{array}{r} 10 \\ +6 \\ \hline \end{array}$$

13.
$$\begin{array}{r} 10 \\ +5 \\ \hline \end{array}$$

14.
$$\begin{array}{r} 10 \\ +2 \\ \hline \end{array}$$

 Writing and Reasoning  Frank
looks at his Workmat. He says the number sentence that
tells about it is $10 + 6 = 16$. Is he correct? Explain
why or why not.

_____

_____

Hands On: Make a Ten to Add

Problem of the Day ———————————————— NS 1.4

Write a number sentence. Show 10. Show 5 more.

Use Workmat 3 and counters to check your answer.

Algebraic Thinking Review ———————————— AF 1.1

Emma has eighteen bracelets. She gave three to
her friends. Write a number sentence to show how
many bracelets Emma has left.

Words of the Day ———————————————— MG 1.1

Use *heavy, heavier, heaviest, lightest.*
Describe how these are related.

    a bicycle, a car, a truck, an airplane

Which is heaviest? Which is lightest?

Complete the sentence.

    A ____ is heavier than a ____. A ____ is lighter than a ____.

Facts Practice ———————————————— KEY NS 2.1

Subtract.

1. $6 - 5 =$ _____
2. $6 - 4 =$ _____
3. $5 - 1 =$ _____
4. $8 - 7 =$ _____
5. $4 - 4 =$ _____

Hands On: Make a Ten to Add

CA Standards
KEY NS 2.1, MR 1.2

Use Workmat 3 and ◯. Make a ten.
Find the sum.

1. Show 8 and 7 more.

$8 + 7 = $ _____

2. Show 6 and 8 more.

$6 + 8 = $ _____

3. Show 9 and 3 more.

$9 + 3 = $ _____

4. Show 7 and 9 more.

$7 + 9 = $ _____

Add.

5.
$$\begin{array}{r} 8 \\ + 8 \\ \hline \end{array}$$

6.
$$\begin{array}{r} 6 \\ + 8 \\ \hline \end{array}$$

7.
$$\begin{array}{r} 9 \\ + 4 \\ \hline \end{array}$$

8.
$$\begin{array}{r} 7 \\ + 9 \\ \hline \end{array}$$

9.
$$\begin{array}{r} 9 \\ + 7 \\ \hline \end{array}$$

10.
$$\begin{array}{r} 7 \\ + 6 \\ \hline \end{array}$$

11.
$$\begin{array}{r} 7 \\ + 8 \\ \hline \end{array}$$

12.
$$\begin{array}{r} 3 \\ + 8 \\ \hline \end{array}$$

13.
$$\begin{array}{r} 5 \\ + 9 \\ \hline \end{array}$$

14.
$$\begin{array}{r} 9 \\ + 2 \\ \hline \end{array}$$

Writing and Reasoning Sara has 7 green hair bows and 5 blue hair bows. Tell how making a 10 will help her figure out how many hair bows she has in all.

_____

_____

Add Three Numbers

Problem of the Day
KEY NS 2.1

Make a 10. Find the sum. Use Workmat 3 and
counters to check your answer.

$$\begin{array}{c} 9 \\ +3 \\ \hline \end{array} \qquad \begin{array}{c} 3 \\ +9 \\ \hline \end{array}$$

Algebraic Thinking Review
AF 1.1

You have 12 colored pencils. You lose 4 of them.
Write a number sentence to show how many
colored pencils you have left.

Counting Activity
KEY NS 2.4

Start at 2. Count by 2s to 30.
Are all these numbers even?
Start at 1. Count by 2s to 31.
Are all these numbers even? Are they all odd?

Facts Practice
KEY NS 2.1

Add.

1. $1 + 6 =$ _____
2. $7 + 1 =$ _____
3. $1 + 4 =$ _____
4. $7 + 5 =$ _____
5. $5 + 5 =$ _____

171

Add Three Numbers

CA Standards
KEY NS 2.1, NS 2.7

Circle the numbers you added first.
Write the sum.

1. $\begin{array}{r} 4 \\ 6 \\ +9 \\ \hline \end{array}$
2. $\begin{array}{r} 5 \\ 2 \\ +5 \\ \hline \end{array}$
3. $\begin{array}{r} 2 \\ 6 \\ +8 \\ \hline \end{array}$
4. $\begin{array}{r} 7 \\ 5 \\ +3 \\ \hline \end{array}$
5. $\begin{array}{r} 9 \\ 1 \\ +3 \\ \hline \end{array}$
6. $\begin{array}{r} 4 \\ 2 \\ +8 \\ \hline \end{array}$

7. $5 + 9 + 3 = $ _____

8. $7 + 0 + 5 = $ _____

9. $2 + 8 + 3 = $ _____

10. $5 + 9 + 4 = $ _____

11. $6 + 3 + 4 = $ _____

12. $5 + 5 + 4 = $ _____

Writing and Reasoning Tell about two
ways you can find the sum of $3 + 3 + 4$.

_____

_____

_____

_____

Name _____ Date _____

Create and Solve

Problem of the Day —————————————————— NS 2.7

Write the sum. Circle the numbers you added first.

```
  9
  3
+ 7          9 + 3 + 7 = _____
___
```

Number Sense Review ———————————— KEY

Which addition helps you check this subtraction?

17 − 9 = 8

Number of the Day ———————————————— KEY

25

Trace 25 in the air.

How many hands does it take to show 25 fingers?

How many children does it take to show 25 fingers?

Facts Practice ——————————————————— KEY

Add.

1. 6 + 4 = _____   2. 0 + 4 = _____

3. 4 + 4 = _____   4. 2 + 8 = _____

5. 3 + 5 = _____

Problem Solving: Create and Solve

CA Standards
KEY NS 2.1, AF 1.3

1. Write an addition sentence for the doubles plus one fact shown in the picture.

_____ ◯ _____ ◯ _____

2. Write an addition sentence for another doubles plus one fact.

_____ ◯ _____ ◯ _____

3. Draw a picture to show your addition sentence.

Writing and Reasoning Write a story to match your doubles plus one fact.

_____

_____

_____

174

Name _____ Date _____

Hands On: Use Doubles to Subtract

Problem of the Day ———————————————————— AF 1.1

Write a number sentence that shows how many
flowers in all.

◯ ___ ___ ◯ ___

Number Sense Review ———————————————————— NS 3.0

There are 25 chickens in the barn and 4 more outside.
About how many chicken are there in all? Estimate.

about 20   about 30

Counting Activity ———————————————————— KEY **NS 1.1**

What number is missing?

17, 18, 19, _____, 21, 22, 23

Facts Practice ———————————————————— KEY **NS 2.1**

Subtract.

1. $7 - 2 =$ _____

2. $5 - 0 =$ _____

3. $11 - 11 =$ _____

4. $5 - 5 =$ _____

5. $11 - 6 =$ _____

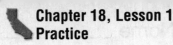
Hands On:
Use Doubles to Subtract

Write a doubles fact.
Use charts and ⬤ to model.
Draw the counters. Write the related subtraction fact.

1.

☐
+ ☐
____
☐

Whole	
Part	**Part**

☐
− ☐
____
☐

2.

☐
+ ☐
____
☐

Whole	
Part	**Part**

☐
− ☐
____
☐

3.

☐
+ ☐
____
☐

Whole	
Part	**Part**

☐
− ☐
____
☐

Writing and Reasoning Why are $9 + 9 = 18$ and $18 - 9 = 9$ related facts?

Subtract From 13 and 14

Problem of the Day ──────────────── KEY NS 2.2

Write a doubles fact.

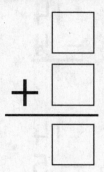
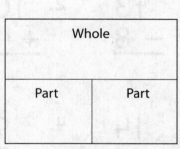

Geometry Review ──────────────── MG 2.2

Circle the shape that is round.

Calendar Activity ──────────────── MG 1.2

Look at the calendar. What is the date of the third
Saturday of this month?

Facts Practice ──────────────── KEY NS 2.1

Subtract.

1. $2 - 0 =$ _____

2. $9 - 1 =$ _____

3. $9 - 7 =$ _____

4. $7 - 2 =$ _____

5. $10 - 10 =$ _____

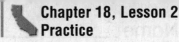

Subtract From 13 and 14

Add. Then find the difference.

1. $\begin{array}{r} 8 \\ +5 \\ \hline \end{array}$ so $\begin{array}{r} 13 \\ -5 \\ \hline \end{array}$ $\begin{array}{r} 13 \\ -8 \\ \hline \end{array}$ 2. $\begin{array}{r} 10 \\ +4 \\ \hline \end{array}$ so $\begin{array}{r} 14 \\ -4 \\ \hline \end{array}$ $\begin{array}{r} 14 \\ -10 \\ \hline \end{array}$

3. $\begin{array}{r} 11 \\ +3 \\ \hline \end{array}$ so $\begin{array}{r} 14 \\ -3 \\ \hline \end{array}$ $\begin{array}{r} 14 \\ -11 \\ \hline \end{array}$ 4. $\begin{array}{r} 9 \\ +5 \\ \hline \end{array}$ so $\begin{array}{r} 14 \\ -5 \\ \hline \end{array}$ $\begin{array}{r} 14 \\ -9 \\ \hline \end{array}$

5. $\begin{array}{r} 8 \\ +6 \\ \hline \end{array}$ so $\begin{array}{r} 14 \\ -6 \\ \hline \end{array}$ $\begin{array}{r} 14 \\ -8 \\ \hline \end{array}$ 6. $\begin{array}{r} 10 \\ +3 \\ \hline \end{array}$ so $\begin{array}{r} 13 \\ -3 \\ \hline \end{array}$ $\begin{array}{r} 13 \\ -10 \\ \hline \end{array}$

7. $\begin{array}{r} 7 \\ +6 \\ \hline \end{array}$ so $\begin{array}{r} 13 \\ -6 \\ \hline \end{array}$ $\begin{array}{r} 13 \\ -7 \\ \hline \end{array}$ 8. $\begin{array}{r} 4 \\ +9 \\ \hline \end{array}$ so $\begin{array}{r} 13 \\ -9 \\ \hline \end{array}$ $\begin{array}{r} 13 \\ -4 \\ \hline \end{array}$

 Writing and Reasoning What addition fact
can help you find $14 - 4$? Explain.

_____

_____

_____

_____

Subtract From 15 and 16

Problem of the Day

Use these three numbers.

7, 5, 12

Write 4 related addition and subtraction facts.

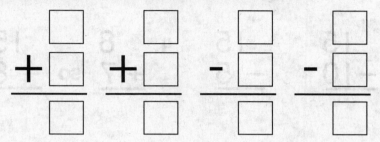

Patterns Review

Tim noticed that the page numbers on the right
pages of his book are: 1, 3, 5, 7, 9, 11, ...
How can Tim figure out the next page number?

Number of the Day

Count on 5 from 35. Then count back 5. Does it make sense that
you end up where you started? Why?

Facts Practice

Add.

1. 8 + 0 = _____   2. 6 + 1 = _____

3. 4 + 4 = _____   4. 8 + 2 = _____

5. 5 + 1 = _____

Subtract From 15 and 16

CA Standards
KEY NS 2.2, **KEY** NS 2.1

Add. Then find the difference.

1. $\begin{array}{r} 11 \\ + 5 \\ \hline \end{array}$ so $\begin{array}{r} 16 \\ -11 \\ \hline \end{array}$ $\begin{array}{r} 16 \\ - 5 \\ \hline \end{array}$ 2. $\begin{array}{r} 9 \\ + 6 \\ \hline \end{array}$ so $\begin{array}{r} 15 \\ - 9 \\ \hline \end{array}$ $\begin{array}{r} 15 \\ - 6 \\ \hline \end{array}$

3. $\begin{array}{r} 10 \\ + 5 \\ \hline \end{array}$ so $\begin{array}{r} 15 \\ -10 \\ \hline \end{array}$ $\begin{array}{r} 15 \\ - 5 \\ \hline \end{array}$ 4. $\begin{array}{r} 8 \\ + 7 \\ \hline \end{array}$ so $\begin{array}{r} 15 \\ - 8 \\ \hline \end{array}$ $\begin{array}{r} 15 \\ - 7 \\ \hline \end{array}$

5. $\begin{array}{r} 6 \\ + 10 \\ \hline \end{array}$ so $\begin{array}{r} 16 \\ - 6 \\ \hline \end{array}$ $\begin{array}{r} 16 \\ - 10 \\ \hline \end{array}$ 6. $\begin{array}{r} 7 \\ + 9 \\ \hline \end{array}$ so $\begin{array}{r} 16 \\ - 7 \\ \hline \end{array}$ $\begin{array}{r} 16 \\ - 9 \\ \hline \end{array}$

Math Journal **Writing and Reasoning** Explain how knowing that $7 + 6 = 13$ can help you find a related subtraction fact.

_____

_____

_____

_____

Subtract From 17 Through 20

Problem of the Day

Add. Then find the difference.

$$9 \qquad 16 \qquad 16$$
$$\underline{+7} \quad \text{so} \quad \underline{-9} \qquad \underline{-7}$$

Algebraic Thinking ———————————— AF 1.1

13 penguins are swimming. 5 went back on land.
Write a number sentence to show how many
penguins are swimming now.

Numbers of the Day

Solve this riddle.

    We are 3 related numbers.
    We can make addition and subtraction sentences together.
    Some call us a family.
    What could we be?

Facts Practice ———————————— KEY NS 2.1

Add.

1. $4 + 2 =$ _____   2. $6 + 3 =$ _____

3. $0 + 9 =$ _____   4. $8 + 6 =$ _____

5. $4 + 0 =$ _____

Subtract From 17 Through 20

Add. Then find the difference.

1.
$$17$$
$$+\ 3$$
so
$$20$$
$$-17$$
$$20$$
$$-\ 3$$

2.
$$9$$
$$+\ 8$$
so
$$17$$
$$-\ 9$$
$$17$$
$$-\ 8$$

3.
$$11$$
$$+\ 6$$
so
$$17$$
$$-11$$
$$17$$
$$-\ 6$$

4.
$$8$$
$$+\ 10$$
so
$$18$$
$$-\ 8$$
$$18$$
$$-\ 10$$

5.
$$5$$
$$+13$$
so
$$18$$
$$-\ 5$$
$$18$$
$$-13$$

6.
$$10$$
$$+\ 10$$
so
$$20$$
$$-\ 10$$
$$20$$
$$-\ 10$$

Writing and Reasoning Pedro has 19 marbles. He gives 9 marbles to Sarah. She says that a subtraction sentence to tell how many marbles Pedro has left is $19 - 10 = 9$. Is she correct? Explain why or why not.

_____

_____

_____

_____

Choose the Operation

Problem of the Day ———————————————— KEY NS 2.2

Add. Then find the difference.

$$\begin{array}{r} 10 \\ + 8 \\ \hline \end{array} \quad \text{so} \quad \begin{array}{r} 18 \\ - 8 \\ \hline \end{array} \quad \begin{array}{r} 18 \\ -10 \\ \hline \end{array}$$

Number Sense Review ———————————————— KEY NS 2.3

Which number is 10 more than 57?

Calendar Activity ———————————————— MG 1.2

Use the calendar.
In what month are we today?
Is it the first month of the year?

Facts Practice ———————————————— KEY NS 2.1

Add.

1. $3 + 4 =$ _____
2. $4 + 9 =$ _____
3. $0 + 1 =$ _____
4. $1 + 4 =$ _____
5. $2 + 2 =$ _____

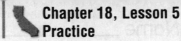
Problem Solving: Choose the Operation

CA Standards
NS 2.0, AF 1.1

Choose the operation to solve.
Write the number sentence.

1. Tyler catches 12 fish on a fishing trip. Sara catches 8 fish. How many fish do they catch in all?

___ ◯ ___ ◯ ___

_____ fish

2. Daniel paints 15 pictures. 7 of the pictures have animals in them. How many pictures do not have animals in them?

___ ◯ ___ ◯ ___

_____ pictures

3. Zach has 14 pieces of gum. He gives 6 pieces away to his friends. How many pieces of gum does he have left?

___ ◯ ___ ◯ ___

_____ pieces

 Writing and Reasoning Look back to Exercise 1. How did you decide which operation to use?

_____

_____

Hands On: Fact Families

Problem of the Day ———————————————— NS 2.0, AF 1.1

Write a number sentence to solve. There are 18 party favors.
There are 12 people at the party. If each guest gets 1 party favor,
how many party favors will be left?

_____ ◯ _____ ◯ _____

Number Sense Review ———————————————— NS 3.0

There are 15 girls and 9 boys in the school band.
About how many children are in the school band?

about 20   about 40

Words of the Day ———————————————— KEY NS 1.1

| even | odd |

Do you have an even number of fingers? Do you have an even
number of noses? Do you have an odd number of eyes?

Facts Practice ———————————————— KEY NS 2.1

Add.

1. 4 + 8 = _____   2. 3 + 8 = _____
3. 10 + 2 = _____   4. 8 + 5 = _____
5. 7 + 3 = _____

Hands On: Fact Families

CA Standards
KEY NS 2.2, NS 2.0

Use Workmat **4** and ⬤ . Complete the fact family.

1.

Whole	
15	
Part	**Part**
8	7

2.

Whole	
12	
Part	**Part**
7	5

3.

Whole	
17	
Part	**Part**
9	8

Writing and Reasoning Harriet says that

$7 + 8$ and $8 - 7$ are part of the same fact family.

Is she correct? Explain why or why not.

_____

Name _____ Date _____

Relate Addition and Subtraction

Problem of the Day ———————————————— KEY NS 2.2

Complete the fact family. Use Workmat 4 and counters if you want.

8	9	☐	☐
+9	+8	−8	+9
☐	☐	9	8

Whole	
Part **9**	Part **8**

Geometry Review ———————————————— MG 2.2

Circle the figure that does not belong.

Number of the Day ———————————————— KEY NS 1.2

Solve this riddle.

Mario lives between house numbers 17 and 22.

Mario lives in a house with an odd number.

Mario's house number is greater than 20.

In which house does Mario live?

Facts Practice ———————————————— KEY NS 2.1

Add.

1. 9 + 4 = _____   2. 8 + 7 = _____

3. 4 + 2 = _____   4. 4 + 7 = _____

5. 6 + 0 = _____

Relate Addition and Subtraction

CA Standards
KEY NS 2.2, KEY NS 2.1

Write the missing numbers.

1. $20 - 10 =$ ____

   $20 = 10 +$ ____

2. $11 - 6 =$ ____

   $11 = 6 +$ ____

3. $15 - 7 =$ ____

   $15 = 7 +$ ____

4. $13 - 8 =$ ____

   $13 = 8 +$ ____

5. $14 - 7 =$ ____

   $14 = 7 +$ ____

6. $12 - 7 =$ ____

   $12 = 7 +$ ____

7. $19 - 10 =$ ____

   $19 = 10 +$ ____

8. $15 - 9 =$ ____

   $15 = 9 +$ ____

9. $16 - 8 =$ ____

   $16 = 8 +$ ____

Writing and Reasoning Karen has 16 crayons in all. She gives 6 crayons to a friend. She says she has 9 crayons left. Is she correct? Explain why or why not.

_____

_____

Name _____ Date _____

Different Ways to Subtract

Problem of the Day ———————————————— KEY NS 2.2

Write the missing numbers to complete the fact family.

_____ + 7 = 16   7 + _____ = 16

16 − 9 = _____   16 − _____ = 9

Patterns Review ———————————————— KEY SDAP 2.1

What is likely to come next in the pattern?

    J, I, M, J, I, M, J, _____

What letters repeat to make the pattern?

Calendar Activity ———————————————— KEY NS 1.1

30

Trace 30 in the air. Look at the calendar.

Are there fewer than, the same as, or more than

30 days this month?

Facts Practice ———————————————— KEY NS 2.1

Subtract.

1. 6 − 6 = _____

2. 6 − 1 = _____

3. 9 − 8 = _____

4. 15 − 4 = _____

5. 11 − 8 = _____

Different Ways to Subtract

CA Standards
KEY NS 2.1, NS 2.0

Write each difference.
Circle the fact if it is related to a doubles fact.

1.
$$16$$
$$-8$$

2.
$$13$$
$$-7$$

3.
$$20$$
$$-10$$

4.
$$18$$
$$-10$$

5.
$$14$$
$$-6$$

6.
$$12$$
$$-6$$

7.
$$15$$
$$-8$$

8.
$$13$$
$$-9$$

9.
$$17$$
$$-7$$

10.
$$14$$
$$-7$$

11.
$$16$$
$$-9$$

12.
$$18$$
$$-9$$

13.
$$10$$
$$-5$$

14.
$$17$$
$$-9$$

15.
$$15$$
$$-5$$

16.
$$13$$
$$-5$$

Writing and Reasoning Joel finds 10 large stones and 9 small stones. He gives 4 stones to his sister. Explain how you can solve to find how many stones Joel has now.

_____

_____

_____

Comparison Problems

Problem of the Day ——————————————————— KEY NS 2.1

Write each difference. Circle the subtraction if it is
related to a doubles fact.

$$\begin{array}{ccc} 15 & 16 & 17 \\ -\ 8 & -\ 8 & -\ 8 \\ \hline \end{array}$$

Algebraic Thinking Review ——————————————— AF 1.1

There are 12 children in Ms. Ireland's class. 3 are girls.
Which number sentence shows how many are boys?

Counting Activity ——————————————————— KEY NS 2.4

Skip count to solve this problem.

　　We are 6 sea stars.

　　We each have 5 arms.

　　How many arms do we have in all?

Facts Practice ——————————————————— KEY NS 2.1

Subtract.

1. $17 - 8 =$ _____

2. $16 - 16 =$ _____

3. $17 - 3 =$ _____

4. $17 - 1 =$ _____

5. $10 - 4 =$ _____

CA Standards
KEY NS 2.1, MR 2.0

Problem Solving: Comparison Problems

Use the comparison bars.

Solve.

1. Sara has **9** apples.

   If she eats **2** apples, she will have the same amount as Keith.

   How many apples does Keith have?

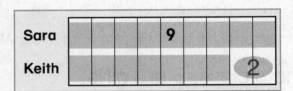

   Keith has _____ apples.

2. David paints **8** pictures.

   If he paints **7** more, he will have as many as Tasha.

   How many paintings does Tasha have?

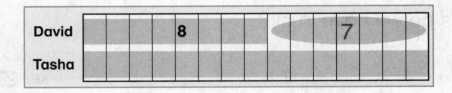

   Tasha has _____ paintings.

Writing and Reasoning Why are comparison bars helpful for solving problems?

_____

_____

Hands On: Coin Values

Problem of the Day
SDAP 1.2

Use the graph.

Who grew more pumpkins? _____
How many more? _____

Number Sense Review
NS 3.1

There are 30 girls and 17 boys in the after-school
art program. About how many more girls than boys
are in the art program?

    about 20 more   about 10 more

Number of the Day
KEY NS 2.4

Skip count to solve this problem.

    We are 10 monkeys.

    We are all hanging from a branch by our toes.

    We each have 10 toes. How many toes are on the branch?

Facts Practice
KEY NS 2.1

Subtract.

1. $12 - 2 =$ _____   2. $4 - 3 =$ _____

3. $15 - 2 =$ _____   4. $13 - 8 =$ _____

5. $17 - 9 =$ _____

Hands On: Coin Values

CA Standards
NS 1.5, MR 1.2

Use coins.

Show 2 different ways to pay for the object.

Draw the coins.

1.

2.

3.

4.

Writing and Reasoning Karolyn has 2 dimes and 3 pennies. She wants to buy an apple for 20¢. Does she have enough money? Explain why or why not.

_____

_____

Name _____ Date _____

Count Nickels

Problem of the Day ———————————————— NS 1.5

What is the value of these coins? _____

How many pennies can you trade for these 2 nickels? _____
How many dimes can you trade for these 2 nickels? _____

Geometry Review ———————————————— MG 2.2

Circle the shape that has the most corners.

Calendar Activity ———————————————— MG 1.2

Look at the calendar. How many days are there
between the first Monday and the third Monday?

Facts Practice ———————————————— KEY NS 2.1

Subtract.

1. $12 - 1 =$ _____   2. $18 - 5 =$ _____
3. $13 - 2 =$ _____   4. $17 - 8 =$ _____
5. $11 - 5 =$ _____

Name _____ Date _____

Hands On: Count Nickels

Use coins.
Find the value of the nickels.

1.

_____¢ _____¢ _____¢   _____¢

2.

_____¢ _____¢ _____¢ _____¢ _____¢   _____¢

3.

_____¢ _____¢ _____¢ _____¢   _____¢

4.

_____¢ _____¢ _____¢ _____¢ _____¢ _____¢   _____¢

 Writing and Reasoning Would you rather have
1 nickel or 3 pennies? Why?

_____

_____

Hands On: Count Nickels and Pennies

Problem of the Day —————————————— KEY NS 2.4, NS 1.5

Count on to find the value of the nickels.

_____ ¢   _____ ¢   _____ ¢   _____ ¢

Patterns Review ————————————————— KEY SDAP 2.1

What repeats to make the pattern?

T, A, M, I, T, A, M, I, T, A, ...

Word of the Day —————————————————— KEY NS 2.1

| doubles |

Give some examples of doubles in addition.
What is special about doubles fact families?

Facts Practice ——————————————————— KEY NS 2.1

Add.

1. 3 + 5 = _____
2. 5 + 4 = _____
3. 6 + 2 = _____
4. 4 + 1 = _____
5. 3 + 3 = _____

Name _____ Date _____

Hands On: Count Nickels and Pennies

CA Standards
NS 1.5, KEY NS 2.4

Circle the coins that match the price.

1.

2.

3.

4.

Writing and Reasoning Duane has **7** nickels and **2** pennies. He wants to buy a magazine for **37**¢. Does he have enough money to but the magazine? Explain.

_____

_____

_____

Count Dimes

Problem of the Day ———————————————— NS 1.5

Find the value of these coins.

_____ ¢

Algebraic Thinking Review ————————————— AF 1.1

There are 8 boys and 9 girls on the soccer team.
Write a number sentence to show how many
children are on the soccer team.

Word of the Day ———————————————— KEY NS 2.4

nickel

There are 6 nickels.
Skip count to find how much they are worth.

Facts Practice ———————————————— KEY NS 2.1

Add.

1. $6 + 5 = $ _____

2. $8 + 9 = $ _____

3. $8 + 4 = $ _____

4. $1 + 12 = $ _____

5. $1 + 2 = $ _____

Count Dimes

Count by 10s.
Find the value of the dimes.

1.

_____¢ _____¢ _____¢ _____¢ _____¢   _____¢

2.

_____¢ _____¢ _____¢   _____¢

3.

_____¢ _____¢ _____¢ _____¢ _____¢ _____¢   _____¢

4.

_____¢ _____¢ _____¢ _____¢ _____¢ _____¢ _____¢   _____¢

 Writing and Reasoning Would you rather have
3 dimes or 5 nickels? Explain.

_____

_____

_____

Count Dimes and Pennies

Problem of the Day ———————————— KEY NS 2.4, NS 1.5

Use coins if you want. Count on to find the value of the dimes.

____ ¢   ____ ¢   ____ ¢   ____ ¢

Money Review ———————————————— NS 1.5

What is the name and value of this coin?

Name: _____   value: _____

Number of the Day ———————————— KEY NS 2.4

50

Say 0. Skip count by 10s from 0 to 50.
How many children have 50 fingers in all? Why?

Facts Practice ———————————————— KEY NS 2.1

Subtract.

1. 4 − 1 = _____
2. 2 − 1 = _____
3. 15 − 14 = _____
4. 15 − 6 = _____
5. 15 − 7 = _____

Name _____ Date _____

Count Dimes and Pennies

Count by tens. Then count by ones.
Write how much in all.

1.

_____¢   _____¢   _____¢   _____¢   _____¢   _____¢

_____¢
in all

2.

_____¢   _____¢   _____¢   _____¢   _____¢   _____¢

_____¢
in all

3.

_____¢   _____¢   _____¢   _____¢   _____¢   _____¢

_____¢
in all

Writing and Reasoning Would you rather
have 2 dimes and 5 pennies or 5 dimes and
2 pennies? Why?

_____

_____

_____

Name _____ Date _____

Create and Solve

Problem of the Day ————————————————— NS 1.5

What is the value of these coins?

_____ ¢

Number Sense Review ————————————— KEY NS 2.4

Count by tens. Which number comes next?

7, 17, 27, 37, 47, _____

Word of the Day ————————————————— NS 1.5

| dime |

What is the value of a dime?

Facts Practice ———————————————————— KEY NS 2.1

Subtract.

1. $15 - 13 =$ _____

2. $12 - 7 =$ _____

3. $14 - 14 =$ _____

4. $14 - 13 =$ _____

5. $6 - 4 =$ _____

Problem Solving:
Create and Solve

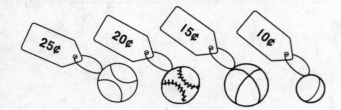

1. Choose **2** balls from the picture.
   How much would they cost together?
   Complete the addition sentence.

   _____ ¢ + _____ ¢ = _____ ¢

2. Choose **2** other balls from the picture.
   How much would they cost together?
   Complete the addition sentence.

   _____ ¢ + _____ ¢ = _____ ¢

3. Choose **2** balls from the picture.
   Write a subtraction sentence showing which ball costs more.

   _____ ¢ − _____ ¢ = _____ ¢

4. Choose **2** other balls from the picture.
   Write a subtraction sentence showing which ball costs more.

   _____ ¢ − _____ ¢ = _____ ¢

Writing and Reasoning Janelle has **50**¢. She wants to
buy a baseball and a tennis ball. Does she have enough money?
Explain why or why not.

_____

_____

Hands On: Count Coins

Problem of the Day —————————————————— NS 1.5

Look at the toys.

How much do they cost in all? _____ ¢

Number Sense Review ————————————————— NS 3.1

Pedro watched 2 music videos. One lasted 15 minutes. The other lasted 27 minutes. About how many minutes did he spend watching videos?

about 40   about 60

Money ——————————————————————————— NS 1.5

How many pennies make a fair trade for a dime?

Facts Practice ———————————————————— KEY NS 2.1

Subtract.

1. 2 – 2 = _____   2. 8 – 4 = _____
3. 9 – 3 = _____   4. 5 – 2 = _____
5. 4 – 1 = _____

Hands On: Count Coins

Use your coins to model.
Write how much in all.

1. ____¢ ____¢ ____¢ ____¢ ____¢ ____¢   ____¢

2. ____¢ ____¢ ____¢ ____¢ ____¢ ____¢ ____¢ ____¢   ____¢

3. ____¢ ____¢ ____¢ ____¢ ____¢ ____¢ ____¢   ____¢

4. ____¢ ____¢ ____¢ ____¢ ____¢ ____¢   ____¢

Writing and Reasoning Carla has 3 dimes, 3 nickels, and 4 pennies. Can she buy an apple that costs 49¢? Explain.

_____

_____

Count Coins

Problem of the Day _____

NS 1.5

Count the coins. How much money is there in all?

_____¢

Geometry Review _____

MG 2.2

Circle the figure that has the fewest corners.

Word of the Day _____

NS 1.5

nickel

How much is a nickel worth? _____
How much are 3 nickels worth? Skip count to find
the answer.

5¢, _____¢ , _____¢

How many nickels does it take to make 25¢? _____

Facts Practice _____

KEY NS 2.1

Add.

1. 5 + 3 = _____   2. 6 + 7 = _____   3. 1 + 16 = _____

4. 1 + 1 = _____   5. 6 + 3 = _____

Equal Amounts

Draw two ways to show each amount.

1. 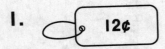 12¢

2. 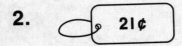 21¢

3.  36¢

 **Writing and Reasoning** Sumey has 5
coins. The value of her coins is 25¢. What coins
does Sumey have? Explain how you know.

_____

_____

_____

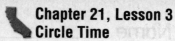
Quarters and Equal Amounts

Problem of the Day NS 1.5

Draw two ways to show this amount.

17¢

Patterns Review ——— KEY SDAP 2.1

Which is NOT a repeating pattern? Explain why.

M A N A N A N A N

A N A N A N A N A

Number of the Day ——— KEY NS 2.3

49

Trace 49 in the air.

What number comes just before 49?

What number comes just after 49?

What number is 10 more than 49?

Facts Practice ——— KEY NS 2.1

Write the number that is 2 more.

1. 16 _____
2. 9 _____
3. 7 _____
4. 10 _____
5. 23 _____

Quarters and Equal Amounts

CA Standards
NS 1.5, KEY NS 2.4

Circle the coins that match the price.

1.

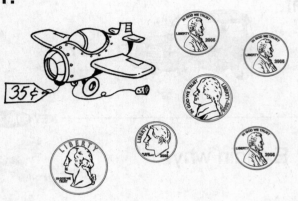

2.

3.

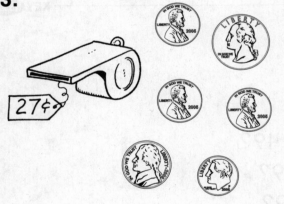

4.

![Math Journal] **Writing and Reasoning** Would you rather have 1 quarter, or 4 dimes, or 7 nickels?

_____

_____

Make a List

Problem of the Day

NS 1.5

Circle the coins that match the price.

Algebraic Thinking

AF 1.1

There were 46 passengers on the bus. 7 left.
Write a number sentence to show how many
passengers are left on the bus.

Words of the Day

MG 1.1

most	least

Think about a bathtub, a swimming pool, or the ocean.
Which holds the *least* water? Which holds the *most* water?
Which is in between?

Facts Practice

KEY NS 2.1

Subtract.

1. 5 − 3 = _____
2. 10 − 1 = _____
3. 9 − 2 = _____
4. 8 − 2 = _____
5. 7 − 1 = _____

Problem Solving: Make a List

Make a list to show the same amount in different ways. Draw the coins.

1. 35¢

_____

_____

2. 20¢

_____

_____

List the coins you would use to show the specified amounts.

3. 17¢ _____   4. 55¢ _____

_____   _____

5. 67¢ _____   6. 43¢ _____

                                        _____

Writing and Reasoning Micah shows 25¢ with 2 dimes and 1 nickel. Can you tell another way to show 25¢?

_____

_____

Use with text pp. 409–410

Hands On: Order Events

Problem of the Day ———————————————— NS 1.5

Make a list that shows the amount in two ways.

30¢

Number Sense Review ————————————— NS 3.1

There are 30 skateboards and 45 bicycles at a sport shop. About how many is that in all?

about 70   about 100

Counting ——————————————————— KEY NS 1.1

Count on 5 from 43. Count back 5 from 43.

Facts Practice ————————————————— KEY NS 2.1

Subtract.

1. $18 - 8 =$ _____
2. $15 - 6 =$ _____
3. $11 - 9 =$ _____
4. $18 - 11 =$ _____
5. $15 - 9 =$ _____

Hands On: Order Events

Write **1**, **2**, and **3** to show the order.

1.		
☐	☐	☐

2.		
☐	☐	☐

3.		
☐	☐	☐

Writing and Reasoning What do you do before you go to bed? What do you do after you wake up?

_____

_____

Compare Time

Problem of the Day ———————————————— MG 1.2

Order the events. Write 1 next to the one you do
first. Write 3 next to the one you do last.

Putting on your shoes _____

Tying your shoelaces _____

Putting on your socks _____

Geometry Review ———————————————— MG 2.4

Name the shape that is *above* the star.

Number of the Day ———————————————— KEY NS 1.2

Solve this riddle.

I am a even number.

I am less than 20.

But I am greater than 16!

Who am I?

Facts Practice ———————————————— KEY NS 2.1

Subtract.

1. $9 - 8 =$ _____   2. $18 - 2 =$ _____

3. $18 - 6 =$ _____   4. $6 - 6 =$ _____

5. $14 - 6 =$ _____

Compare Time

Look at each picture.
Circle the correct word to compare if each
activity is shorter or longer than an hour.

1.  shorter longer	 shorter longer
2.  shorter longer	 shorter longer

Writing and Reasoning What are some
things that take longer than an hour to do?

_____

_____

Hour

Problem of the Day ——————————— MG 1.2

Circle the best answer. What takes longer?

    Going to school

    Being at school

Patterns Review ——————————— KEY SDAP 2.1

What comes next in the pattern?

    I   II   2I   3I   _____

Words of the Day ——————————— MG 1.2

Use the words *minutes* or *hours* to answer.

    It takes about 2 _____ to brush your teeth.

    It takes about 9 _____ to sleep at night.

    It takes about I _____ to eat dinner.

    It takes about 3 _____ to put on socks and shoes.

Facts Practice ——————————— KEY NS 2.1

Subtract.

1. $7 - 4 =$ _____
2. $14 - 11 =$ _____
3. $12 - 0 =$ _____
4. $7 - 4 =$ _____
5. $12 - 3 =$ _____

Hour

CA Standard
MG 1.2

Read the clock.
Write the time two ways.

1.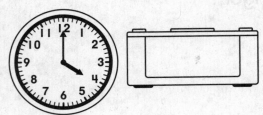

_____ o'clock

2.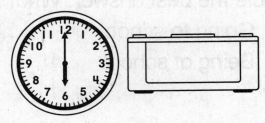

_____ o'clock

3.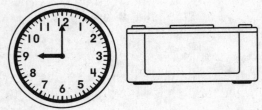

_____ o'clock

4.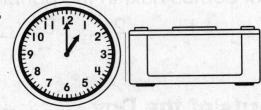

_____ o'clock

5.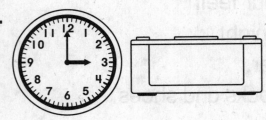

_____ o'clock

6.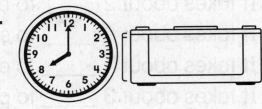

_____ o'clock

Writing and Reasoning How far around the
clock does the minute hand move in 1 hour? How far
around the clock does the hour hand move in 1 hour?

_____

_____

Name _____ Date _____

Half Hour

Problem of the Day ———————————————— MG 1.2

Write the time two ways.

____ : ____

____ o'clock

Algebraic Thinking Review ———————————————— AF 1.1

There were 8 passengers on the bus. 7 more passengers came on. Write a number sentence to show how many passengers are now on the bus.

Words of the Day ———————————————— MG 1.2

Which is longer, 1 hour or 30 minutes?

Facts Practice ———————————————— KEY NS 2.1

Subtract.

1. $16 - 4 =$ _____   2. $14 - 5 =$ _____

3. $15 - 11 =$ _____   4. $11 - 4 =$ _____

5. $13 - 3 =$ _____

Half Hour

Say and write the time.

1.

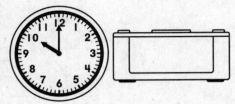

_____ o'clock

2.

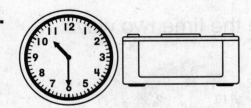

half past _____

3.

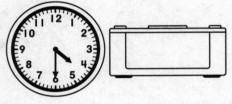

half past _____

4.

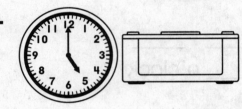

_____ o'clock

5.

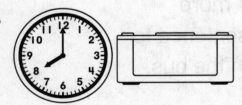

_____ o'clock

6.

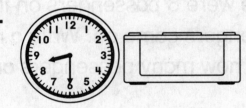

half past _____

 Writing and Reasoning Look at Exercise 3.

Why is the longer hand on the 6?

_____

_____

_____

_____

Name _____ Date _____

Use a Table

Problem of the Day ———————————————— MG 1.2

Write the time two ways.

_____ : _____

half past _____

Number Sense Review ———————————————— KEY NS 2.5

When a question asks how many in all, do you add,
subtract, or compare?

Calendar Activity ———————————————— MG 1.2

Use the calendar. How many school days are there
in this month?

Facts Practice ———————————————— KEY NS 2.1

Add.

1. 13 + 4 = _____   2. 5 + 9 = _____

3. 5 + 10 = _____   4. 9 + 0 = _____

5. 11 + 6 = _____

Name _____ Date _____

Problem Solving: Use a Table

Solve. Use information from the table.

The Big Top Circus Schedule	
Event	Times
Pony Rides	9:00
Elephant Walk	10:30
Trapeze Act	12:30
Clowns	2:00

1. What activity starts $3\frac{1}{2}$ hours after the pony rides?

   _____

2. How many hours are there between the elephant walk and the trapeze act?

   _____

3. Drew arrives at the circus at 8:00. He is looking forward to a pony ride. How long does he have to wait?

   _____

4. The trapeze act is about to start. How long does Aria have to wait until the clowns come out?

   _____

Writing and Reasoning How many hours are between the elephant walk and the trapeze act? Explain.

_____

Hands On: Add a 2-Digit Number and a 1-Digit Number

Problem of the Day ————————————————— MG 1.2

This is the morning schedule.

When does the reading period start? _____
When does the next subject start? _____
How long is the reading period? _____

Start Time	
Reading	9:00
Math	10:00
Writing	10:30

Number Sense Review ————————————————— NS 3.1

65 people went to the dolphin show. 30 people went to the sea lion show. About how many more people went to the dolphin show than the sea lion show?

about 30 more   about 100 more

Numbers of the Day ————————————————— NS 1.0

How are 15 and 51 alike?
How are they different?

Facts Practice ————————————————— KEY NS 2.1

Subtract.

1. $17 - 1 =$ _____   **2.** $13 - 6 =$ _____   **3.** $15 - 9 =$ _____

4. $16 - 6 =$ _____   **5.** $14 - 1 =$ _____

Hands On: Add a 2-Digit Number and a 1-Digit Number

Use Workmat 3 and **.**

Solve.

1. $12 + 6 = $ _____

2. $14 + 2 = $ _____

3. $13 + 4 = $ _____

4. $17 + 1 = $ _____

Add.

Count on from the greater addend.

5. $\begin{array}{r} 13 \\ + 3 \\ \hline \end{array}$

6. $\begin{array}{r} 14 \\ + 5 \\ \hline \end{array}$

7. $\begin{array}{r} 11 \\ + 4 \\ \hline \end{array}$

8. $\begin{array}{r} 12 \\ + 3 \\ \hline \end{array}$

9. $\begin{array}{r} 13 \\ + 4 \\ \hline \end{array}$

10. $\begin{array}{r} 15 \\ + 3 \\ \hline \end{array}$

11. $\begin{array}{r} 17 \\ + 2 \\ \hline \end{array}$

12. $\begin{array}{r} 14 \\ + 3 \\ \hline \end{array}$

13. $\begin{array}{r} 16 \\ + 2 \\ \hline \end{array}$

14. $\begin{array}{r} 15 \\ + 5 \\ \hline \end{array}$

 Writing and Reasoning Sheri is adding $12 + 4$. How can she count on to find the sum?

_____

_____

Hands On: Add 2-Digit and 1-Digit Numbers with Regrouping

Problem of the Day ——————————————— NS 2.6

Use Workmat 3 and counters if you want.

$$12 + 6 = \underline{\hspace{2cm}}$$

$$\begin{array}{r} 6 \\ + 12 \\ \hline \end{array}$$

Geometry Review ——————————————— MG 2.4

Name the figure that is below the star.

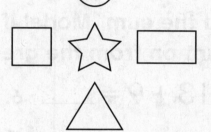

Words of the Day ——————————————— NS 1.5

| penny | nickel | dime | quarter |

Which coin is worth 1 cent?

Which coin is worth 5 cents?

What is the name of the smallest coin?

What is the name of the largest coin?

Facts Practice ——————————————— KEY NS 2.1

Add 5 to each number.

1. 1 _____   2. 9 _____   3. 7 _____

4. 8 _____   5. 15 _____

Hands On: Add 2-Digit and 1-Digit Numbers with Regrouping

CA Standards
KEY NS 2.5, NS 2.6

Use Workmat 3, ⬜, and ⚫ .
Solve.

1. Show 15. Add 6 more

   ____ + ____ = ____

2. Show 17. Add 5 more

   ____ + ____ = ____

3. Show 18. Add 7 more

   ____ + ____ = ____

4. Show 16. Add 7 more

   ____ + ____ = ____

Find the sum. Model if you wish.
Count on from the greater addend.

5. $13 + 9 =$ ____

6. $15 + 8 =$ ____

7. $17 + 7 =$ ____

8. $14 + 6 =$ ____

9. $16 + 6 =$ ____

10. $19 + 5 =$ ____

Math Journal **Writing and Reasoning** Marlee adds 14 fish to the tank. Jim adds 7 fish to the tank. Marlee says there are 25 fish in the tank in all. Is she correct? Explain why or why not.

_____

_____

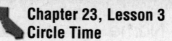
Sums to 30

Problem of the Day ———————————————— NS 2.6

Use Workmat 3, blocks, and counters if you want.
Show 19. Add 8 more. Write the number sentence.

_____ + _____ = _____

Patterns Review ——————————————— KEY SPAP 2.1

A bird is chirping.

   Chi, Chi, Choo, Chi, Chi, Choo, Chi, Chi, Choo, Chi, ...
What is the pattern unit that repeats?

Calendar Activity ——————————————— MG 1.2

Use the calendar.
What month are we in?
Which other months have the same number of days
as this month?

Facts Practice ——————————————— KEY NS 2.1

Add.

1. $4 + 13 =$ _____   **2.** $0 + 6 =$ _____   **3.** $9 + 1 =$ _____

4. $4 + 5 =$ _____   **5.** $8 + 5 =$ _____

Sums to 30

Circle the basic fact.
Then find the sum.

1. Find $15 + 7$.

$$10 + \underline{\quad} + \underline{\quad}$$

$$10 + \boxed{} = \underline{\quad}$$

2. Find $13 + 8$.

$$10 + \underline{\quad} + \underline{\quad}$$

$$10 + \boxed{} = \underline{\quad}$$

3. Find $22 + 4$.

$$20 + \underline{\quad} + \underline{\quad}$$

$$20 + \boxed{} = \underline{\quad}$$

4. Find $18 + 9$.

$$10 + \underline{\quad} + \underline{\quad}$$

$$10 + \boxed{} = \underline{\quad}$$

Find the sum.

5. $16 + 7 = \underline{\quad}$ **6.** $14 + 9 = \underline{\quad}$ **7.** $21 + 7 = \underline{\quad}$

8. $12 + 9 = \underline{\quad}$ **9.** $24 + 5 = \underline{\quad}$ **10.** $17 + 8 = \underline{\quad}$

Writing and Reasoning Mari wants to find
the sum of $18 + 7$. Explain how she can find it
using mental math.

_____

_____

Guess and Check

Problem of the Day ———————————————— NS 2.6

Circle the basic fact. Find the sum.

17 + 9

10 + _____ + _____

10 + ☐ = _____

Number Sense Review ———————————————— NS 2.6

Todd read 5 pages today, 12 pages yesterday, and
8 pages the day before.

How many pages has he read in all?

Number of the Day ———————————————— KEY

| 100 |

Tell what you know about the number 100.

Facts Practice ———————————————— KEY

Subtract.

1. 16 − 6 = _____   2. 10 − 8 = _____

3. 7 − 7 = _____   4. 8 − 6 = _____

5. 9 − 8 = _____

Name _____ Date _____

Problem Solving: Guess and Check

Guess and check to solve.

Crayon Boxes			
A	B	C	D
12	24	45	52

I. Sophie takes 2 boxes with 57 crayons to her friends. Which 2 boxes does she take?

Draw to explain.

box _____ and box _____

2. Leando gives away 64 crayons. Which 2 boxes does he give away?

box _____ and box _____

Writing and Reasoning Jose and Fredrico want 76 crayons. Explain how you can solve to find the boxes they should buy.

_____

_____

_____

_____

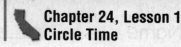
Hands On: Model Addition to 50

Problem of the Day ———————————————————————— NS 2.6, NS 3.1

Guess the sum.

19 + 9

About how much is 19? about _____

About how much is 9? about _____

About how much is the sum? about _____

Check if your guess is correct. 19 + 9 = _____

Is your guess close to the exact answer? _____

Money Review ———————————————————————————— NS 3.1, NS 1.5

Tami has 3 quarters. Does she have more or less
than 90¢? How do you know?

Counting Activity ——————————————————————————— KEY **NS 2.4**

Count by twos from 1 to 59.

Numerical Fluency ——————————————————————————— KEY **NS 2.1**

Find the number that is 2 less.

1. 15 _____

2. 17 _____

3. 10 _____

4. 28 _____

5. 14 _____

Hands On: Model Addition to 50

CA Standards
NS 2.6, KEY NS 2.5

Use Workmat 5 with ▭▭▭▭▭ and ▱.
Regroup. Write the sum.

1. $27 + 7 =$ _____

2. $34 + 8 =$ _____

3. $18 + 8 =$ _____

4. $29 + 5 =$ _____

5. $22 + 9 =$ _____

6. $36 + 5 =$ _____

7. $25 + 7 =$ _____

8. $19 + 9 =$ _____

Writing and Reasoning Noah has 26 pennies. He is going to make groups of 10. How many single pennies will be left after he regroups them?

_____

_____

Sums to 50

Problem of the Day ————————————————————— NS 2.6

Use Workmat 5 and ▭▭▭▭▭ and ▪ if you want.
Regroup.
Write the sum.

36 + 7 = _____

Geometry Review ———————————————————————— MG 2.4

Circle the figure that is to the right of the star.

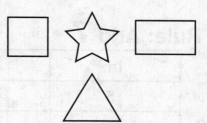

Words of the Day ————————————————————— KEY NS 2.1

Listen to the story. Is it an in all story or a take away story?

Polly had 4 library books.

She took 2 back to the library.

How many library books does Polly have left?

This is a _____ story.

Facts Practice ——————————————————————— KEY NS 2.1

Add or subtract.

1. 0 + 7 = _____   2. 5 + 3 = _____   3. 3 + 5 = _____
4. 13 − 5 = _____   5. 12 − 8 = _____

Sums to 50

Add to complete the chart.

Rule: Add 8

	In	Out
1.	27	
2.	21	
3.	32	
4.	18	

Rule: Add 9

	In	Out
5.	22	
6.	37	
7.	41	
8.	23	

Rule: Add 7

	In	Out
9.	15	
10.	28	
11.	34	
12.	25	

Rule: Add 6

	In	Out
13.	27	
14.	34	
15.	25	
16.	39	

Writing and Reasoning Karl has 18 ones blocks. How many ones will be left after he regroups?

_____

_____

Hands On: Model Addition to 100

Problem of the Day
NS 2.6

Add to complete the chart.

Add 8	
In	Out
30	
31	
32	
33	
34	

Patterns Review
KEY SDAP 2.1

What repeats in the pattern?

    dime dime nickel nickel dime dime nickel nickel
    dime dime nickel nickel...

Calendar Activity
MG 2.1

Use the calendar.

Which month has the fewest number of days? _____

Facts Practice
KEY NS 2.1

Subtract.

1. $4 - 4 =$ _____
2. $4 - 1 =$ _____
3. $5 - 5 =$ _____
4. $9 - 6 =$ _____
5. $7 - 5 =$ _____

Hands On: Model Addition to 100

CA Standards
KEY NS 2.5, NS 2.6

Use Workmat **5** with ▭▭▭▭▭ and ▱.
Regroup. Write the sum.

1. $67 + 5 =$ _____

2. $74 + 8 =$ _____

3. $59 + 5 =$ _____

4. $83 + 8 =$ _____

5. $62 + 8 =$ _____

6. $56 + 5 =$ _____

7. $75 + 7 =$ _____

8. $48 + 4 =$ _____

Writing and Reasoning Ella has 65 pennies. She finds 8 more pennies. How many pennies does she have now? Explain how you can solve using regrouping.

_____

_____

_____

Sums to 100

Problem of the Day

Use Workmat 5 and  and _____ if you want.
Regroup.
Write the sum.

75 + 9 = _____

Algebraic Thinking Review

What subtraction sentence is in the same fact
family as 8 + 9 = 17?

Number of the Day

18

Trace 18 in the air.
Are you older than 18?
Is your mother older than 18?
Do you have a brother or sister that is 18?

Facts Practice

Add.

1. 5 + 8 = _____   2. 6 + 5 = _____   3. 3 + 14 = _____
4. 0 + 7 = _____   5. 5 + 9 = _____

Sums to 100

CA Standards
NS 2.6, NS 2.0

Solve.

Regroup if you need to.

1. $82 + 7 =$ _____

2. $76 + 8 =$ _____

3. $79 + 4 =$ _____

4. $62 + 3 =$ _____

5. $82 + 8 =$ _____

6. $54 + 7 =$ _____

7. $75 + 3 =$ _____

8. $49 + 5 =$ _____

 Writing and Reasoning Jerome is adding $78 + 3$. He says that he does not have to regroup. Is he correct? Explain why or why not.

_____

_____

Find a Pattern

Problem of the Day ———————————————————————— NS 2.6

Solve.

Regroup if you need to.

57 + 7 = _____

7 + 57 = _____

Number Sense Review ——————————————————— KEY NS 2.5

When a question asks how many are left, do you
add, subtract, or compare?

Word of the Day ——————————————————————— KEY NS 2.2

| fact family |

Solve this riddle.

We are a fact family.

I am 8 + 3 = 11

My brother is 11 − 3 = 8

My sister is 3 + 8 = 11

Who is my other brother?

Facts Practice ——————————————————————————— KEY NS 2.1

Add.

1. 4 + 6 = _____

2. 9 + 7 = _____

3. 7 + 1 = _____

Problem Solving: Find a Pattern

Find the pattern. Complete the table.

Then use the table to answer the questions.

Number of Cows	Number of Legs
1	4
2	8
3	12
7	
	32

1. Sara visits the Dairy Farm. She sees 20 legs in the barn.

How many cows does she see? _____ cows

2. How many legs do 2 cows have? _____ legs

3. How many legs do 7 cows have? _____ legs

Writing and Reasoning Henry wants to know how many legs 9 cows have. What is a quick way to find the answer?

_____

_____

_____

Hands On: Subtract a 1-Digit Number from a 2-Digit Number

Problem of the Day —————————————————

Nan's family gets 5 magazines each week.

How many magazines will they have at the end of 5 weeks?

Complete the table.

Magazines	
Weeks	Magazines
1	5
2	
3	
4	
5	

Algebraic Thinking Review ————————————— KEY NS 2.1

Which is more 12 − 3 or 15 − 8?

Word of the Day ————————————————————— MG 1.2

half hour

How many minutes are in 1 half hour?

Facts Practice —————————————————————

Add.

1. 1 + 9 = _____   2. 7 + 4 = _____   3. 3 + 13 = _____

4. 0 + 16 = _____   5. 4 + 8 = _____

Hands On: Subtract a 1-Digit Number from a 2-Digit Number

Use charts with ▱▱▱▱ and ▱ to subtract.
Write the difference.

1.

Tens	Ones
1	7
−	5

2.

Tens	Ones
2	9
−	5

3.

Tens	Ones
2	9
−	5

4.

Tens	Ones
3	8
−	4

5.

Tens	Ones
3	5
−	4

6.

Tens	Ones
2	6
−	5

7.

Tens	Ones
4	9
−	7

8.

Tens	Ones
5	7
−	3

Writing and Reasoning There are 37 children in the school band. 4 children play the tuba. Explain how you can solve to find how many children in the school band play other instruments.

_____

_____

_____

_____

Hands On: Subtract from Numbers to 50

Problem of the Day ———————————————— NS 2.6

Use Workmat 5 and ▨▨▨▨▨ and ▪
if you want.
Subtract. Write the difference.
33 − 2 = _____

tens	ones
3	3
	2

Geometry Review ———————————————— MG 2.4

Name the figure that is to the left of the star.

Words of the Day ———————————————— MG 1.1

taller	shorter

Who is taller, you or your teacher?
Which is shorter, your desk or the teacher's desk?

Facts Practice ———————————————— KEY NS 2.1

Add.

1. 1 + 11 = _____   2. 4 + 3 = _____   3. 4 + 11 = _____
4. 9 + 1 = _____   5. 0 + 0 = _____

Name _____ Date _____

Hands On:
Subtract from Numbers to 50

Use Workmat **5**, ⬚⬚⬚⬚⬚⬚, and ⬚.
Regroup if needed.
Subtract. Write the difference.

1. $33 - 7 = $ _____   2. $45 - 4 = $ _____

3. $39 - 5 = $ _____   4. $42 - 6 = $ _____

5. $44 - 9 = $ _____   6. $36 - 2 = $ _____

7. $32 - 8 = $ _____   8. $41 - 3 = $ _____

 Writing and Reasoning Look at Exercise **2**.
Do you need to regroup? Explain why or why not.

_____

_____

_____

Hands On: Model Subtraction from Numbers to 100

Problem of the Day

Subtract. Write the difference.

$32 - 9 =$ _____

Patterns Review

What repeats to make the pattern?

Numbers of the Day

Which is more money: a 10-dollar bill or a
100-dollar bill? Which takes less time to watch:
a 10-minute video or a 100-minute movie?

Facts Practice

Subtract.

1. $4 - 3 =$ _____   2. $14 - 12 =$ _____

3. $12 - 7 =$ _____   4. $15 - 9 =$ _____

5. $8 - 4 =$ _____

Name _____ Date _____

Hands On: Model Subtraction from Numbers to 100

CA Standards
KEY NS 2.5, NS 2.6

Use Workmat **5** with ⬚⬚⬚⬚ and ⬚.
Regroup if needed. Subtract.

1.

Tens	Ones
☐	☐
6	5
−	8

2.

Tens	Ones
☐	☐
7	9
−	4

3.

Tens	Ones
☐	☐
8	1
−	6

4.

Tens	Ones
☐	☐
5	4
−	7

5.

Tens	Ones
☐	☐
7	5
−	9

6.

Tens	Ones
☐	☐
6	7
−	8

7.

Tens	Ones
☐	☐
5	7
−	4

8.

Tens	Ones
☐	☐
8	8
−	8

Writing and Reasoning Brad is solving
$78 - 9$. Does he need to regroup? Explain why
or why not.

_____

_____

Name _____ Date _____

Subtract from Numbers to 100

Problem of the Day ——————————————————— NS 2.6

Use Workmat 5 and ▨▨▨▨▨ and ▪ if you want.
Subtract. Write the difference.

$90 - 9 =$ _____

tens	ones
9	0
−	9

Algebraic Thinking Review ——————————————— AF 1.3

Circle the story that matches this number sentence.

$12 + 6 = 18$

Tony had 12 strawberries. He ate 6 of them.
Tony had 12 strawberries. He got 6 more.
Tony had 18 strawberries. He got 12 more.

Calendar Activity ——————————————————— MG 1.2

Look at the calendar.

Does the calendar tell you about weight?
Does the calendar tell you about length?
Does the calendar tell you about time?

Facts Practice ——————————————————— KEY NS 2.1

Subtract.

1. $9 - 2 =$ _____   2. $5 - 2 =$ _____   3. $4 - 4 =$ _____

4. $8 - 5 =$ _____   5. $7 - 4 =$ _____

Name _____ Date _____

Subtract from Numbers to 100

**Look at the problem. Circle do or don't.
Subtract.**

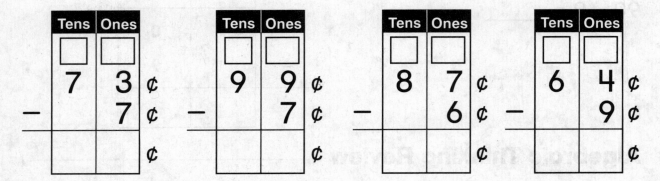

1. I do / don't regroup. **2.** I do / don't regroup. **3.** I do / don't regroup. **4.** I do / don't regroup.

Tens	Ones
☐	☐
7	3 ¢
−	7 ¢
	¢

Tens	Ones
☐	☐
9	9 ¢
−	7 ¢
	¢

Tens	Ones
☐	☐
8	7 ¢
−	6 ¢
	¢

Tens	Ones
☐	☐
6	4 ¢
−	9 ¢
	¢

5. I do / don't regroup. **6.** I do / don't regroup. **7.** I do / don't regroup. **8.** I do / don't regroup.

Tens	Ones
☐	☐ ¢
8	6 ¢
−	7 ¢

Tens	Ones
☐	☐ ¢
7	7 ¢
−	7 ¢

Tens	Ones
☐	☐ ¢
5	2 ¢
−	4 ¢

Tens	Ones
☐	☐ ¢
6	5 ¢
−	8 ¢

Writing and Reasoning To subtract 7 from 79 do you need to regroup? Explain why or why not.

_____

_____

Problem Solving Field Trip

Problem of the Day —————————————————— NS 2.6

Subtract. Write the difference.

78 − 9 = _____

tens	ones
7	8
−	9

Number Sense Review ———————————————— NS 2.6

What is the sum?

```
   58
 +  7
 ————
```

Word of the Day ————————————————— KEY NS 2.5

subtract

When do you subtract?

Facts Practice ——————————————————— KEY NS 2.1

Add.

1. 2 + 10 = _____   2. 0 + 4 = _____

3. 6 + 8 = _____   4. 10 + 7 = _____

5. 1 + 15 = _____

Hands On: Position Words

Problem of the Day ———————————————— NS 2.6

Write a number sentence. Then solve.

    There are 36 penguins at the zoo.

    9 are swimming.

    How many penguins are not swimming?

            _____ ◯ _____ ◯ _____

Number Sense Review ———————————————— NS 3.1

The plane can seat 78 people. There are 31 empty

seats. How many passengers are in the plane?

    about 50   about 100

Word of the Day ———————————————— MG 1.1

measuring tools

What can you use to measure the length of your book?

What can you use to measure how heavy your book is?

How can you find how many pages are in your book?

Facts Practice ———————————————— KEY NS 2.1

Subtract.

1. $15 - 9 =$ _____   2. $4 - 1 =$ _____   3. $9 - 9 =$ _____

4. $14 - 4 =$ _____   5. $17 - 0 =$ _____

Hands On: Position Words

Read the directions.

Draw the object.

1. Draw an 🌰 to the right of the 🐿️ .

2. Draw a ☀️ above the 🌳 .

3. Draw a 🌸 between the 🏠 and the ⌂ .

4. Draw 3 🥚 below the 🌳 .

Writing and Reasoning Think about the chair you are sitting on. Use position words to describe its location.

_____

_____

More Position Words

Problem of the Day ———————————————— MG 2.3

What is above the star? _____
What is below the star? _____
What is to the right of the star? _____
What is to the left the star? _____

Geometry Review ———————————————— MG 2.4

What is the name the shape that is in front?

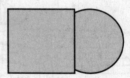

Word of the Day ———————————————— NS 1.5

coins

What are the coins people use to buy things?
What is the value of a penny?
What is the value of a nickel?
What is the value of a dime?
What is the value of a quarter?

Facts Practice ———————————————— KEY NS 2.1

Add.

1. 2 + 6 = _____   2. 2 + 4 = _____   3. 12 + 6 = _____
4. 4 + 4 = _____   5. 0 + 2 = _____

More Position Words

CA Standards
MG 2.3, MG 2.4

Circle the answer that completes the sentence.

1.

The 🐕 is _____ the 🏠.

in front of   behind

2.

The 🐾 is _____ the 🌳.

up   below

3.

The ⛵ is _____ the 🛳.

far from   near

4.

The 🐱 is _____ the 🐶.

far from   next to

 Writing and Reasoning Use the word "near" to describe where you are sitting in the classroom.

_____

_____

Plane Figures

Problem of the Day ———————————————— MG 2.4

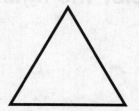

What is next to the star? _____
What is far from the star? _____
What is behind the star? _____

Data Review ————————————————————— SDAP 1.2

Which fruit is preferred the most?

Preferred Fruit	
Apple	卌
Orange	|||
Strawberry	卌 ||

Calendar Activity ———————————————— KEY NS 1.1

Use the calendar.

Count. How many days are there in two weeks?

Facts Practice ———————————————————— KEY NS 2.1

Add.

1. $7 + 6 =$ _____   2. $13 + 1 =$ _____   3. $7 + 4 =$ _____

4. $13 + 4 =$ _____   5. $2 + 13 =$ _____

Circle Time/Practice

255

Use with Chapter 26, Lesson 3

Name _____ Date _____

Plane Figures

CA Standard
MG 2.1, MG 2.0

Answer the questions.
Color the figures on the sailboat.

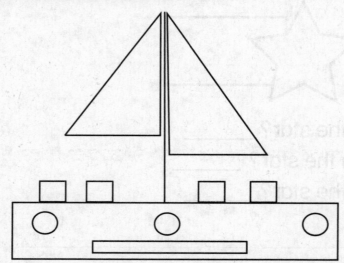

1. How many figures have
   3 sides? _____
   Color the triangles
    Red .

2. How many figures
   have **0** sides? _____
   Color the circles
   Green .

3. How many figures have
   4 sides that are not all the
   same size? _____
   Color the rectangles
   Yellow .

4. How many figures have
   4 sides that are all the
   same? _____
   Color the squares
   Blue .

Writing and Reasoning Look at a circle.
What makes it different than the other plane figures?

_____

_____

Sort Plane Figures

Problem of the Day ———————————————— MG 2.1

How many figures have 4 sides? _____

What is the name of the figure that is curved? _____

What is the name of the figure that is longer than it is wide? _____

Algebraic Thinking Review ———————————— AF 1.1

100 people attended the school fair.

75 were children.

Write a number sentence to show how many

people at the fair were NOT children.

Calendar Activity ———————————————— KEY NS 1.1

How many days are there from today to the

end of next month?

How many weeks?

Facts Practice ————————————————————— KEY NS 2.1

Subtract.

1. $10 - 2 =$ _____   2. $8 - 6 =$ _____

3. $14 - 4 =$ _____   4. $17 - 7 =$ _____

5. $7 - 2 =$ _____

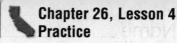
Sort Plane Figures

Read the sorting rule.

Circle the figures that follow the rule.

1. At least 3 corners

2. 3 corners

3. More than 3 sides

4. 4 equal sides

 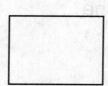 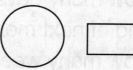

Writing and Reasoning Jeff has these figures
◯, △, and ☐. His sorting rule is figures with less
than 4 sides. Do all Jeff's figures fit this rule? Explain
why or why not.

_____

_____

Find a Pattern

Problem of the Day ———————————— MG 2.2

Circle all the shapes that have more than 3 sides.

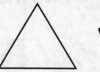

Number Sense Review ———————————— NS 2.6

What is the difference?

$$
\begin{array}{r}
95 \\
-\ \ 9 \\
\hline
\end{array}
$$

Calendar Activity ———————————— NS 1.0

Use the calendar.

Point to today's date.

Write the number that is today's date.

Facts Practice ———————————— KEY NS 2.1

Add.

1. 2 + 10 = _____   2. 5 + 8 = _____

3. 4 + 4 = _____   4. 2 + 9 = _____

5. 7 + 9 = _____

Problem Solving: Find a Pattern

CA Standard
KEY SDAP 2.1

Find the pattern to solve.

1. Thalia sees this pattern on a blanket.
   Circle the one that comes next.

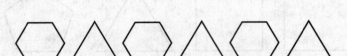

2. Doug sees this pattern on a book cover.
   Circle the one that comes next.

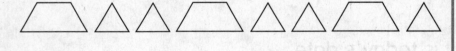

3. Arnitra sees this pattern on a painting.
   Circle the one that comes next.

Writing and Reasoning Mario makes this
pattern with shapes. ▱▢▱▢▱▢. He
is going to put a ▱ next. Is he correct? Explain
why or why not.

_____

_____

Hands On: Sort Solid Figures

Problem of the Day ———————————————— KEY **SDAP 2.1**

Draw the figure that is likely to come next.

  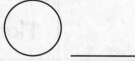 _____

Algebraic Thinking Review ———————————— AF 1.3

Circle the story that matches the number sentence.

75¢ − 15¢ = 60¢

A Tom had 3 quarters and spent 15¢.

B Tom has 3 quarters and 15¢.

C Tom has 3 dimes and 3 nickels.

Words of the Day ———————————————— MG 2.1

| curved | straight |

Use your arm to show a curved shape in the air.

Use your arm to show a shape with straight sides
in the air.

Facts Practice ———————————————————— KEY **NS 2.1**

Subtract.

1. 12 − 0 = _____   2. 15 − 3 = _____   3. 18 − 8 = _____

4. 17 − 2 = _____   5. 17 − 9 = _____

Hands On: Sort Solid Figures

Use solid figures.
Complete the table.

	Flat Surfaces	Curved Surfaces	Corners
I. ⬤			
2. ◻			
3. ⬭			
4. ▱			
5. △			

Writing and Reasoning Can you slide a sphere? Explain why or why not.

_____

_____

_____

Solid Figures

Problem of the Day ————————————————— MG 2.2

Circle the figures that have flat surfaces.

Cross out the figures that have corners.

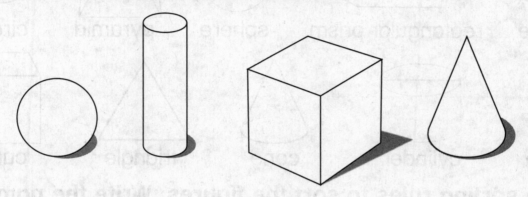

Geometry Review ————————————————— MG 2.4

Name the figure that is behind the square.

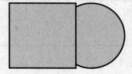

Counting Activity ————————————————— KEY NS 2.4

Start at 2.

Skip count by 2s to 40.

Numerical Fluency ————————————————— KEY NS 2.3

Write the number that is 10 more.

1. 28____   2. 47____   3. 36____   4. 29____   5. 6____

Name _____ Date _____

Solid Figures

CA Standards
MG 2.2, SDAP 1.1

Color each solid figure below.

rectangle

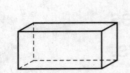
rectangular prism

sphere

pyramid

circle

square

cylinder

cone

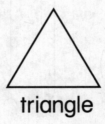
triangle

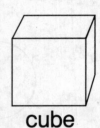
cube

Use the sorting rules to sort the figures. Write the names.

1.   **Plane Figures**

2.   **Solid Figures**

_____   _____

_____   _____

_____   _____

_____   _____

_____   _____

Writing and Reasoning Sam draws this
picture ☐. He says it is a cube. Is he correct?
Explain why or why not.

_____

_____

_____

Use with text pp. 517–518

Identify Faces of Solid Figures

Problem of the Day ———————————— MG 2.1

Read the sorting rule.

Rule: All flat surfaces

Circle the figures that follow the rule.

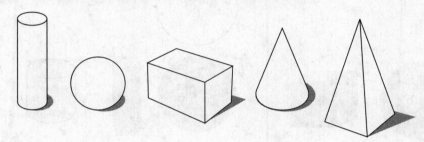

Data Review ———————————————— SDAP 1.1

How are these figures sorted?

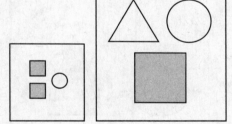

Calendar Activity ——————————— KEY NS 1.1

How many days are there between the first
Tuesday and the fourth Tuesday of this month?

Facts Practice ————————————— KEY NS 2.1

Subtract.

1. 12 − 1 = _____   2. 15 − 4 = _____

3. 16 − 8 = _____   4. 11 − 7 = _____

5. 2 − 1 = _____

Identify Faces of Solid Figures

**Look at the plane figure. Circle the solid with
a face like it.**

1.

2.

3.

4.

Writing and Reasoning Betty has a . She
says one of the faces is a square. Is she correct?
Explain why or why not.

_____

_____

_____

Problem Solving: Make a Table

Problem of the Day ——————————————— MG 2.1

All of my faces are rectangles.
Circle me.

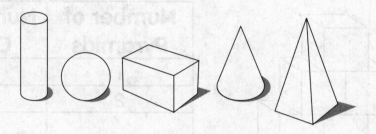

Algebraic Thinking Review ——————————— AF 1.1

There are 77 people in the room.
9 more people join them. Write a number sentence
to show how many people are in the room now.

Words of the Day ——————————————— MG 1.2

| morning | noon | evening |

When do you get up? _____
When do you eat lunch? _____
When do you go to bed? _____

Facts Practice ——————————————— KEY NS 2.1

Subtract.

1. 6 − 3 = _____   2. 10 − 8 = _____   3. 2 − 0 = _____

4. 6 − 5 = _____   5. 7 − 4 = _____

Problem Solving: Make a Table

CA Standards
KEY NS 2.4, SDAP 1.0

Complete the tables. Solve.

1. Seth is using cubes to build pyramids.
   How many cubes will he need to build **5** pyramids like
   this one?

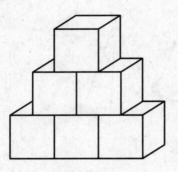

Number of Pyramids	Number of Cubes
1	
2	
4	

_____ cubes

2. Jasmine is using blocks to make houses.
   She is going to make **3** houses like this one shown.

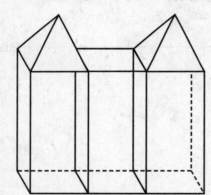

Number of Houses	Number of Rectangular Prisms	Number of Square Pyramids
1		
2		
3		

Writing and Reasoning Jasmine wants to
build a fourth house. How many rectangular prisms
does she need now? Explain how you know.

_____

_____

Hands On: Compare Length and Height

Problem of the Day ——————————————— KEY NS 2.4

Frank is building a wall of cubes.

His wall is made stacks of cubes.

Each stack is 5 cubes tall.

How many cubes are in 7 stacks?

Complete the table.

Stacks	1	2	3	4	5	6	7
Cubes	5						

Number Sense Review ——————————————— NS 3.1

Mrs. Verduzco baked 8 dozen, or 96, cookies.

She gave 35 to her neighbor. Estimate. About how

many cookies does she have left?

about 20   about 60   more than 100

Counting Activity ——————————————— KEY NS 1.1

Say 37. Count on 3 from 37.

Facts Practice ——————————————— KEY NS 2.1

Subtract.

1. $17 - 0 =$ _____   2. $1 - 1 =$ _____   3. $9 - 0 =$ _____

4. $10 - 2 =$ _____   5. $7 - 6 =$ _____

Hands On: Compare Length and Height

CA Standards
MG 1.1, MG 1.0

Is the object longer or shorter than your hand? Circle.

1.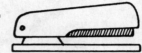

   longer   shorter

2.

   longer   shorter

3.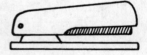

   longer   shorter

4.

   longer   shorter

**Order your objects from shortest to longest.
Number the pictures.**

5.

   ____   ____   ____   ____

Writing and Reasoning Can an object be longer than one person's hand and shorter than another person's hand? Explain.

_____

_____

_____

Hands On: Nonstandard Units

Problem of the Day ——————————————— MG 1.1

Order from shortest to tallest.
Write 1 under the shortest object.
Write 3 under the tallest one.

_____   _____   _____

Geometry Review ——————————————— MG 2.4

Name the figure that is below the line.

Calendar Activity ——————————————— KEY NS 1.1

Use the calendar.
Count. How many days are there in three weeks?

Facts Practice ——————————————— KEY NS 2.1

Add.

 + 2 = _____   + 5 = _____

 + 1 = _____   ▪ + 17 = _____

+ 10 = _____

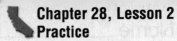

Hands On: Nonstandard Units

Choose a unit to measure the length.

Find the object.	Record the measure.	Circle the unit.
1.	about _____	
2.	about _____	
3.	about _____	
4.	about _____	

Writing and Reasoning Suppose you measure an object with small clips and then again with large clips. Would the measurement change? Explain.

_____

_____

_____

Hands On: Compare Weight

Problem of the Day ——————————————— MG 1.0

Use cubes.

How many cubes long is your desk? _____

Data Review ——————————————— SDAP 1.2

Use the graph.

Which kind of music got the fewest votes?

Preferred Music	
Country	卌
Rock	卌 II
Rap	卌 I

Word of the Day ——————————————— KEY NS 2.2

fact family

What facts are in the family for 6, 5, and 11?

Facts Practice ——————————————— KEY NS 2.1

Add.

1. $2 + 8 =$ _____   2. $0 + 10 =$ _____

3. $9 + 3 =$ _____   4. $7 + 3 =$ _____

5. $3 + 11 =$ _____

Hands On: Compare Weight

CA Standards
MG 1.1, MG 1.0

Find the object. Circle the heavier object.

1.

2.

3.

4.

5.

6.

7.

8.

Writing and Reasoning Bob thinks that an apple is heavier than a peanut. How can he find out if he is correct?

_____

_____

_____

274
Use with text pp. 535–536

Hands On: Compare Volume

Problem of the Day ——————————————— MG 1.1

Circle the object that is the heaviest.
Cross out the object that is the lightest.

Algebraic Thinking Review ——————————— AF 1.3

Which story matches this number sentence?

$65 - 11 = 54$

A   Zack has 65 raisins. He gets 11 more.

B   Zack has 65 raisins. Mara has 11 more raisins than Zack.

C   Zack has 65 raisins. Mara has 11 raisins. How many more raisins does Zack have than Mara?

Calendar Activity ——————————————— MG 1.2

Use the calendar.

    What month are we in?

    What will next month be?

    What was last month?

Facts Practice ——————————————— KEY NS 2.1

Subtract.

1. $7 - 6 =$ _____   2. $15 - 2 =$ _____   3. $16 - 6 =$ _____

4. $9 - 6 =$ _____   5. $9 - 5 =$ _____

Hands On: Compare Volume

CA Standards
MG 1.1, MG 1.0

Circle the container that can hold more.

1.

2.

3.

4.

Circle the container that can hold less.

5.

6.

7.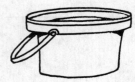

8.

Writing and Reasoning Tara wants to put water from her cup into a bowl. How does she know if it will all fit?

_____

_____

_____

Problem Solving: Use a Graph

Problem of the Day ———————————————— MG 1.1

Which can hold more?
Circle it.

Number Sense Review ———————————————— NS 2.7

What is the sum?

$$
\begin{array}{r}
8 \\
9 \\
+\ 4 \\
\hline
\end{array}
$$

Number of the Day ———————————————— KEY NS 2.4

30

Skip count by 2s to 30.

Facts Practice ———————————————— KEY NS 2.1

Subtract.

1. 4 − 2 = _____   2. 17 − 15 = _____   3. 13 − 1 = _____
4. 7 − 2 = _____   5. 16 − 9 = _____

Problem Solving: Use a Graph

CA Standards
SDAP 1.2, MG 1.1

Use a graph to solve.

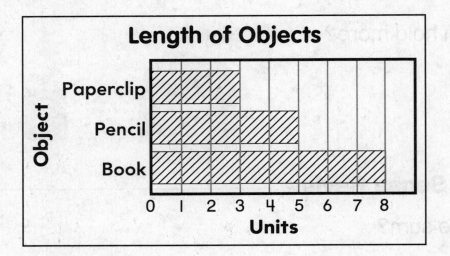

Length of Objects

1. How many more units long is the book than the paper clip?

   _____ more units

2. How many units are the pencil and book in all?

   _____ units

3. How many units in all are the paper clip, pencil, and book?

   _____ units

4. How many more units long is the book than the pencil?

   _____ more units

 Writing and Reasoning Look at Exercise 2.

How did you find your answer?

_____

_____

_____

Looking Ahead Activities

**These activities will help you
get ready for math next year.**

Ten More, Ten Less

CA Standards
KEY NS 2.3; prepares
for Gr. 2 KEY NS 2.2

By yourself

Materials:
place-value blocks

You can use the words **more than** and
less than to tell about 10 more and 10 less.

11	12	13	14	15	16	17	18	19	20
21	22	23	24	25	26	27	28	29	30
31	32	33	34	35	36	37	38	39	40
41	42	43	44	45	46	47	48	49	50
51	52	53	54	55	56	57	58	59	60
61	62	63	64	65	66	67	68	69	70
71	72	73	74	75	76	77	78	79	80

28 is 10 less than 38.

48 is 10 more than 38.

Use ▭▭▭▭ and ▫. **Show the number.**
Show 10 more or 10 less. Write the number.

1. 10 less than 24

14
24

_1_ ten _4_ ones

2. 10 more than 32

32

___ tens ___ ones

3. 10 less than 67

67

___ tens ___ ones

Write the addition and subtraction sentences
that show ten more and ten less.

4.

36
46
56

$46 - 10 = 36$
$46 + 10 = 56$

5.

53

___ ___ = ___   ___ ___ = ___
___ ___ = ___   ___ ___ = ___

6.

71

___ ___ = ___   ___ ___ = ___
___ ___ = ___   ___ ___ = ___

Objective: Use place value to identify 10 more and 10 less than a given number.

Name _____ Date _____

Coins

CA Standards
NS 1.5; prepares for
Gr. 2 **KEY** NS 5.1

With your partner

Materials:
coins

A money amount can be shown in
different ways.

One Way

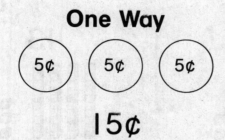

15¢

Another Way

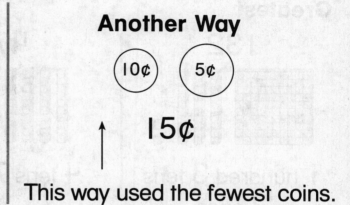

15¢

This way used the fewest coins.

Model the amount using the fewest coins.
Draw a quick picture of the coins.

1. 20¢
2. 30¢
3. 35¢

Objective: Use the fewest number of coins to show an amount.

Order and Compare Numbers

CA Standards
KEY NS 1.2; prepares
for Gr. 2 **KEY** NS 1.3

| **With a small group** |
| **Materials:** place-value blocks |

You can put numbers in order.

Greatest   **Least**

132   47   43

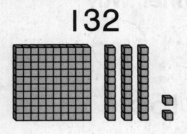

1 hundred 3 tens
2 ones

132 has a
hundred, so it
is greater than
47 and 43.

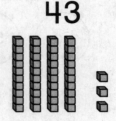

4 tens 7 ones

47 has
more ones
than 43.

4 tens 3 ones

**Use place-value blocks. Show each number. Order
from greatest to least. Draw quick pictures to show the
order. Write the number below each quick picture.**

1. 15, 18, 121

_____   _____   _____

2. 86, 103, 94

_____   _____   _____

Objective: Order and compare numbers using place value.

Name _____ Date _____

Use Symbols to Compare Numbers

You can use symbols to show how numbers compare.

< is less than
= is equal to
> is greater than

CA Standards
KEY NS 1.2; prepares
for Gr. 2 **KEY** NS 1.3

With your partner

Materials:
place-value blocks

2 tens 9 ones   is greater than   2 tens 6 ones
      29   >   26

Use ▭▭▭▭ and ◻. Show each number. Draw quick pictures. Compare. Write <, =, or >.

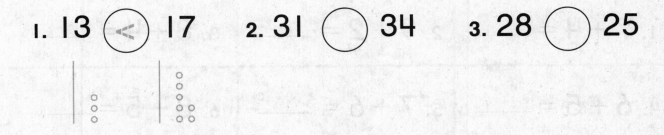

1. 13 (<) 17   2. 31 ( ) 34   3. 28 ( ) 25

4. 21 ( ) 19   5. 30 ( ) 32   6. 46 ( ) 36

Objective: Compare two-digit numbers using <, =, >.

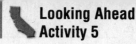

Teen Facts

Find $8 + 3$.

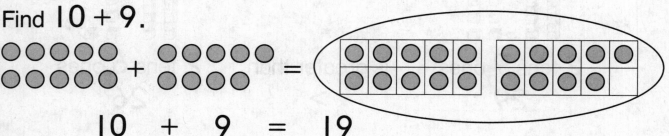

$8 + 3 = 11$

Find $10 + 9$.

$10 + 9 = 19$

CA Standards
KEY NS 2.1; prepares
for Gr. 2 **KEY** NS 2.2

With your partner

Materials:
Two-color counters,
Workmat 3

Find each sum. Use ⚫ and Workmat 3 to help.

1. $7 + 4 = $ _____	2. $9 + 2 = $ _____	3. $8 + 4 = $ _____
4. $6 + 5 = $ _____	5. $7 + 6 = $ _____	6. $8 + 5 = $ _____
7. $9 + 3 = $ _____	8. $6 + 6 = $ _____	9. $9 + 9 = $ _____
10. $9 + 10 = $ _____	11. $10 + 8 = $ _____	
12. $8 + 10 = $ _____	13. $9 + 8 = $ _____	

Objective: Find sums for facts for 11, 12, 13, 17, 18, and 19.

More Teen Facts

CA Standards
KEY NS 2.2; prepares
for Gr. 2 KEY NS 2.2

With your partner

Find $9 + 5$.

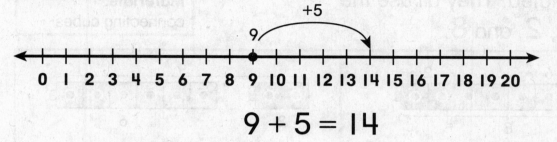

$$9 + 5 = 14$$

Find each sum. Use a number line to help.

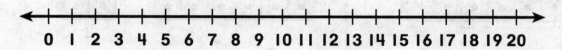

1. $9 + 6 =$ _____	2. $8 + 6 =$ _____	3. $7 + 8 =$ _____
4. $9 + 7 =$ _____	5. $8 + 9 =$ _____	6. $9 + 4 =$ _____
7. $8 + 7 =$ _____	8. $7 + 9 =$ _____	9. $8 + 8 =$ _____
10. $7 + 7 =$ _____	11. $5 + 9 =$ _____	12. $6 + 9 =$ _____
13. $9 + 5 =$ _____	14. $6 + 8 =$ _____	15. $9 + 8 =$ _____

Objective: Find sums for facts for 13, 14, 15, 16, and 17.

Related Facts

These addition facts and subtraction facts are related. They all use the numbers 6, 2, and 8.

CA Standards
KEY NS 2.2; prepares
for Gr. 2 **KEY** NS 2.1

With your partner

Materials:
connecting cubes

6 2 $6 + 2 = 8$ 8	8 2 6 $8 - 6 = 2$
2 6 $2 + 6 = 8$ 8	8 6 2 $8 - 2 = 6$

Complete the number sentences.

1. $3 + 4 = $___ $7 - 4 = $___
   $4 + 3 = $___ $7 - 3 = $___

2. $1 + 5 = $___ $6 - 5 = $___
   $5 + 1 = $___ $6 - 1 = $___

3. $5 + 3 = $___ $8 - 3 = $___
   $3 + 5 = $___ $8 - 5 = $___

4. $2 + 7 = $___ $9 - 7 = $___
   $7 + 2 = $___ $9 - 2 = $___

5. $4 + 5 = $___ $9 - 5 = $___
   $5 + 4 = $___ $9 - 4 = $___

6. $6 + 4 = $___ $10 - 4 = $___
   $4 + 6 = $___ $10 - 6 = $___

Objective: Find how addition and subtraction facts are related.

Place Value

The same number can be shown in
different ways.

CA Standards
NS 1.4; prepares for
Gr. 2 NS 1.2

With your partner

Materials:
place-value blocks

34

3 tens 4 ones

34

2 tens 14 ones

Use ▭▭▭ **and** ▫ **.**
Show the number in another way.

1. 25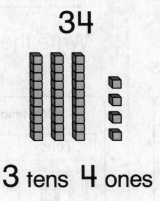

2 tens 5 ones

Draw your blocks.

Write how many.

_____ tens _____ ones

2. 46

4 tens 6 ones

Draw your blocks.

Write how many.

_____ tens _____ ones

Objective: Show a number in different ways using tens and ones.

Name _____ Date _____

Addition Problems

With your class

Materials:
Workmat 5,
place-value blocks

Add **38 + 5.**

Show **38**. Show **5**.	Add the ones. **8** ones + **5** ones	Write the sum.
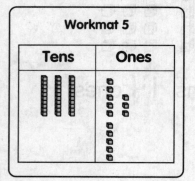	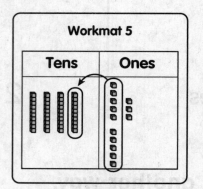	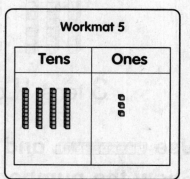
	There are **10** more ones. Regroup **10** ones as **1** ten.	**4** tens **3** ones **43**

38 + 5 = 43

Use Workmat 5, ▭▭▭▭ **and** ◻ **. Add.
Regroup 10 ones as 1 ten. Write the sum.**

1. 25 + 7 = _____	2. 39 + 5 = _____
3. 17 + 6 = _____	4. 46 + 8 = _____
5. 58 + 4 = _____	6. 64 + 9 = _____

Objective: Add using place-value blocks.

Subtraction Problems

CA Standards
NS 2.6; prepares for Gr. 2
KEY NS 2.2

With your class

Materials:
Workmat 5,
place-value blocks

Subtract 42 – 8.

Show 42.	Try to take away 8 ones.	Subtract the ones. Write the difference.
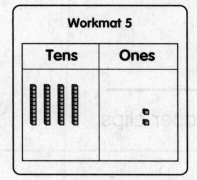	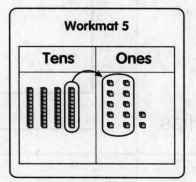	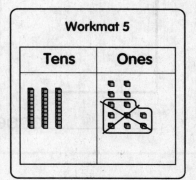
	There are not enough ones. Regroup 1 ten as 10 ones.	3 tens 4 ones 34

42 – 8 = 34

**Use Workmat 5, ⬚⬚⬚⬚ and ▢ .
Subtract. Write the difference.**

1. 35 – 7 = _____	2. 43 – 6 = _____
3. 28 – 9 = _____	4. 41 – 5 = _____
5. 36 – 8 = _____	6. 54 – 8 = _____

Objective: Subtract using place-value blocks.

Measure Length

Measure each L shape using 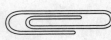.

CA Standards
MG 1.1; prepares
for Gr. 2 MG 1.1

With your partner
Materials: small paper clips, objects to measure

1.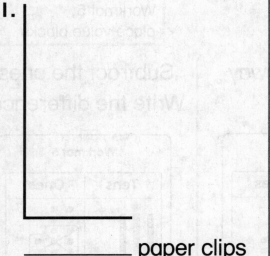

_____ paper clips

2.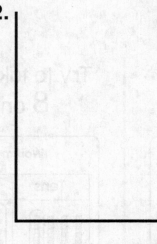

_____ paper clips

3.

_____ paper clips

4.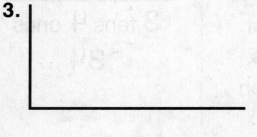

_____ paper clips

**5. Look around the classroom for objects
that are about 3 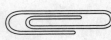 long.**

Name the objects below.

_____

_____

_____

Objective: Estimate and measure length using small paper clips.

Name _____ Date _____

Quarter Hour

CA Standards
MG 1.2; prepares for Gr. 2 MG 1

Each 15 minutes is a quarter hour.

With your class

 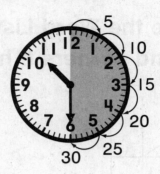 

quarter past 10   half past 10   quarter to 11

15 minutes after 10   30 minutes   45 minutes
                      after 10   after 10

10:15   10:30   10:45

Write the times.

1.

: _____

2.

: _____

3.

: _____

4.

: _____

Objective: Tell time to the quarter hour.

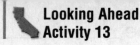
Describe Two-Dimensional Shapes

CA Standards
MG 2.1, MG 2.2;
prepares for Gr. 2 **KEY** **MG 2.1**

With your class

Name each shape. Use the Word List.
Tell how many sides and corners it has.

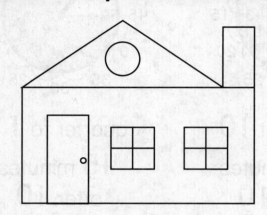

Word List

triangle
square
rectangle
circle

1. △ This shape is a

_____

It has _____ sides.
It has _____ corners.

2. ☐ This shape is a

_____

It has _____ sides.
It has _____ corners.

3. ◯ This shape is a

_____

It has _____ sides.
It has _____ corners.

4. ▭ This shape is a

_____

It has _____ sides.
It has _____ corners.

Objective: Describe two-dimensional shapes.

Name _____ Date _____

Describe Three-Dimensional Shapes

Look at these shapes.

sphere cube cylinder cone rectangular prism pyramid

Identify each three-dimensional shape by answering the riddle.

1. I am a shape that . . .
   * has two faces shaped like a circle
   * can slide
   * can roll

   What shape am I?

   _____

2. I am a shape that . . .
   * has a face that is a square
   * has all the same faces
   * has 6 sides

   What shape am I?

   _____

3. I am a shape that . . .
   * has 0 faces
   * can roll

   What shape am I?

   _____

4. I am a shape that . . .
   * has a face that is a square
   * has 4 faces that are triangles

   What shape am I?

   _____

Objective: Compare and contrast three-dimensional shapes according to their attributes.

Compare Two- and Three-Dimensional Shapes

CA Standards
MG 2.1, MG 2.2;
prepares for Gr. 2 **KEY** MG 2.1

With your partner

Materials:
three-dimensional
shapes, paper

**Use three-dimensional shapes.
Trace the gray face of each shape.
Use the shape and your drawing to
fill in the blanks.**

1.  A rectangular prism has _____ faces,
_____ edges, and _____ corners.

The face is a _____. It has
_____ sides and _____ corners.

2. A pyramid has _____ faces, _____
edges, and _____ corners.

The face is a _____. It has
_____ sides and _____ corners.

3. 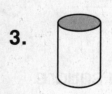 A cylinder has _____ faces,
_____ edges, and _____ corners.

The face is a _____. It has
_____ sides and _____ corners.

Objective: Compare two- and three-dimensional shapes.

Name _____ Date _____

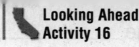

Explore Repeating Patterns

A repeating pattern is a pattern that repeats over and over again.

(1 3 5) 1 3 5 1 3 5

The circle shows the part of the pattern that repeats.

Write the next number to continue each pattern.

1. 2 4 6 2 4 6 2 4 6 _____

2. 1 3 1 3 1 3 1 3 1 _____

3. 3 7 7 3 7 7 3 7 7 _____

Use the repeating pattern to find the missing number. Write the missing numbers in each pattern.

4. 8 8 6 8 8 6 8 __ 6

5. 4 2 4 2 4 2 __ 2 4 __

6. 1 3 __ 1 3 5 1 __ 5 1

Write a repeating pattern. Circle the part that repeats.

7.

Objective: Find and extend repeating patterns in numbers.

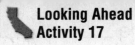
Additive Patterns

CA Standards
SDAP 2.0; prepares
for Gr. 2 SDAP 2.1

By yourself

In some patterns, as one part gets bigger,
the other part gets bigger using a rule.

Each horse has **2** ears. How many
ears do **4** horses have?

You can make a table.

Add **2** ears for each horse to find how many ears **4** horses have.

1 horse	2 horses	3 horses	4 horses
2 ears	4 ears	6 ears	8 ears

2 $2 + 2 =$ $2 + 2 + 2 =$ $2 + 2 + 2 + 2 =$

4 horses have **8** ears.

Find the pattern. Complete the table. Solve.

1. Each chair has **4** legs. How many legs do
   5 chairs have? _____ legs

1 chair	2 chairs	3 chairs	4 chairs	5 chairs
4 legs	_____ legs	_____ legs	_____ legs	_____ legs

2. Write a problem that can be solved by using a pattern and a
   table.

   _____

   _____

   _____

Objective: Find and extend additive patterns in numbers.

Make a Picture Graph

CA Standards
SDAP 1.2; prepares
for Gr. 2 SDAP 1.2

With your partner

Take a survey using one of the questions on the board. Ask 10 classmates to answer your question.

1. Make a tally chart.

2. Use the tally chart to make a picture graph.

Objective: Make a tally chart and a picture graph.

Make a Bar Graph

CA Standards
SDAP 1.2; prepares
for Gr. 2 SDAP 1.2

With your partner

Take a survey using one of the questions on the board. Ask 10 classmates to answer your question.

1. Make a tally chart.

2. Use the tally chart to make a bar graph.

Objective: Make a tally chart and a bar graph.

Name _____ Date _____

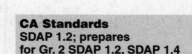

Read a Bar Graph

CA Standards
SDAP 1.2; prepares
for Gr. 2 SDAP 1.2, SDAP 1.4

With your class

Pete makes a bar graph to show the favorite colors of some of his friends.

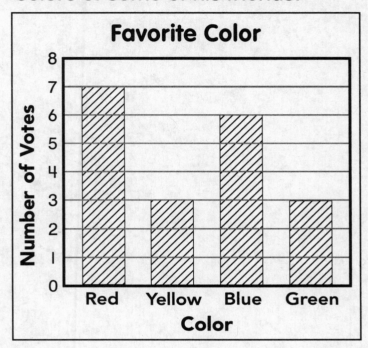

1. What color had the most votes? _____

2. How many children chose blue? _____

3. What two colors did **3** children choose?

_____ _____

4. Which two colors did more than **5** children choose?

_____ _____

5. How many children chose blue or green?

_____ + _____ = _____

6. Write a question that can be answered using the graph. _____

_____

Objective: Draw conclusions and answer questions using a bar graph.

Read a Bar Graph

Pete makes a bar graph to show the favorite colors of some of his friends.

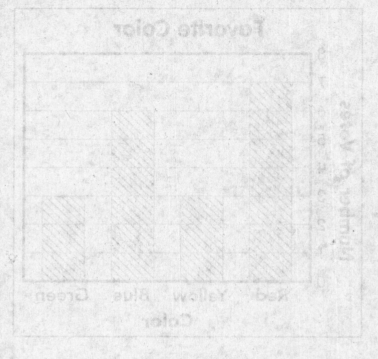

Favorite Color

1. What color got the most votes? _____

2. How many children chose blue? _____

3. What two colors did 3 children choose?

   _____

4. Which two colors did more than 5 children choose?

   _____

5. How many children chose blue or green?

   _____ + _____ = _____

6. Write a question that can be answered using
   the graph.

   _____

Objective 0.8.4, 30A Ask, and answer questions using a bar graph.